NOW READ THIS

William Atkinson is an associate minister at Kensington Temple, one of the largest churches in Britain, where he has been on the pastoral team since 1988. Born and bred in London, William moved to Edinburgh in 1979 to study medicine. Here he met Alison, a fellow medic, and they married in 1983. After working briefly as a doctor, William heard God's call to the ministry and attended Elim Bible College for two years before taking up a position at Kensington Temple. From 1991–1992 he attended London Bible College, gaining a masters degree in theology. In 1993 he became team co-ordinator at the church, a position he still holds.

Now Read This

William Atkinson

KINGSWAY PUBLICATIONS
EASTBOURNE

ISBN 0 85476 544 1

Designed and produced by
Bookprint Creative Services
P.O. Box 827, BN21 3YJ, England for
KINGSWAY PUBLICATIONS LTD
Lottbridge Drove, Eastbourne, E. Sussex BN23 6NT.
Printed in Great Britain.

Contents

Foreword

William Atkinson has a passion for God's word and a desire to help both new believers and mature Christians plumb the depths of its beauty and wealth. *Now Read This*, the practical guide he has written to accomplish this aim, is a refreshing look at this timeless subject.

David the psalmist wrote: 'You have exalted above all things your name and your word' (Psalm 138: 2). At this time, when so many churches are experiencing manifestations of the Holy Spirit's power, it is essential that the Bible has a pre-eminent position, is studied and practically applied to our lives.

William puts what he writes into practice. His commitment to his own marriage, family life and his day-to-day work in pastoral ministry at Kensington Temple reflect his strong convictions and give his writing the ring of integrity.

I warmly recommend *Now Read This!*, whether you have been a Christian for many years or are just starting out on the journey of eternal life. It will not only inspire you to revere and love God's truth but also provide invaluable 'how to's' as you seek to be a doer of the word in every area of your life.

Lyndon Bowring

Acknowledgements

This book would not have come about if it had not been for some important people, whose contributions to its production I would like to acknowledge. Thank you to Wynne Lewis and Dr Joy Seeveratnam, who arranged for me to be whisked off to a tropical island (Penang, Malaysia), where I first had the opportunity to write the material from which this book has evolved. Thanks, too, to Dr Max Turner of London Bible College, who more than anyone else taught me how to understand the Bible. I want to record the help of Dr Jack Hywel-Davies, who put me in touch with my publishers, Kingsway, and offer thanks to Colin Dye, senior minister at Kensington Temple, for his constant encouragement. Special thanks go to my wife Alison, without whom this book would not have achieved its final form. Above all, thanks be to God!

Preface

There are many books available which teach us about how to understand the Bible. Understanding is vital. But, as I am sure all the authors of such books would happily agree, it is only part of a process. In the Bible itself we find the prayer, 'Give me understanding, and I will keep your law and obey it with all my heart' (Psalm 119:34). Here we see understanding viewed as one stage in a process towards obedience. We might go a step further and say that obedience leads towards the eventual goal of the journey, which is that *God might be glorified.* So this book includes a section on how to understand God's word, but it also tries to look at other areas of our relationship with the word of God. We need to know how to relate to his word correctly in all respects. As we do this, *he will perform his word in us,* changing us for his glory and our good, and enabling us to obey it and live by it.

In Mark 12:30 we read the famous words, 'Love the Lord your God with all your heart and with all your soul and with all your mind and with all your strength.' Undoubtedly, reading the Bible is one way of expressing our love for God, so this command must surely include the thought, '*Read the Bible* with all your heart and with all your soul and with all your mind and with all your strength.' In other words, read it with your whole self—

spirit, soul and body all thrown into the process. Therefore the issues involved in handling the Bible will touch *physical, spiritual, and mental* aspects of our lives, and all of these are covered in the chapters of this book.

At the end of each chapter, you will find some questions under the title 'Back to the Bible—for contemplation or discussion'. As the title suggests, you can use these on your own to deepen your thinking about the subjects touched on in the chapter, or you can introduce the questions into discussions held in house groups and small fellowships. Generally, the questions follow the well-known outline of Observation, Interpretation, and Application. This means that the first question is along the lines of, 'What does the passage say?'; the second, 'What does it mean?', and the third, 'How should it make a difference?' This approach to Bible passages forms the outline for the helpful book, *How to Study Your Bible* by Kay Arthur, published in Britain by Kingsway Publications. You will also find some 'sample prayers'. I hope you will read this book prayerfully anyway, but you may find it helpful to be guided in how to respond to God in prayer.

Now read on!

1

Now Read What?

Museums are often full of signs reading, 'Do not touch' and, 'Do not handle'. This is because crowds of interested onlookers cannot be trusted to handle the objects of value without in some way soiling or spoiling them. Children are often told, 'Now be really careful. Don't tip it; don't drop it; hold it as if it were the crown jewels!' We can only be trusted to handle something appropriately once we really know what it is and what it's worth. We handle a tool differently from an ornament. We need to know what the Bible is so that we value it enough to handle it with the respect and spiritual care that it deserves.

Do you know what the Bible is? I would guess that most people reading this book are already committed to the idea that the Bible is the word of God—that it is inspired by God, while written by people. So why write a chapter on this subject? Why be in danger of telling you what you already know? Why try to convince you about what you are already sure of? I have two reasons.

The first is that, while you may be convinced that the Bible is the word of God, you may not really know *why* you believe this. It may be a case of blind faith. But God does not call for blind faith. He gives us evidence in which we can put our faith. Look at the resurrection, for example. We have to put our faith in the fact that it actually happened, but we are presented with evidence that it happened. It is in this evidence that we put our faith. I want to show you the evidence that the Bible is God's own word, but I am not setting out to *prove* it to you. There is no proof. The claim cannot be proved, any more than the resurrection or the virgin birth can be proved. Where there is proof, there is no room for faith, and these are matters of faith (reasonable faith, remember, based on evidence).

The other reason is that, while you may well truly believe that the Bible is the word of God, you may not really know what 'word of God' means. You may not appreciate the relationship between the human and divine activities involved in writing Scripture.

So where do we go to answer these questions? When you want to know what something is, you study the object itself. This may be a quick glance or a full-scale laboratory test. One of my interests is ornithology and I have spent many hours studying birds. I have stood on a narrow causeway between gigantic windswept reservoirs in the middle of winter, trying to keep my binoculars or telescope steady against the biting wind, and straining my eyes to make out the features of some distant dot-like bird, simply to know what it was. It's more comfortable to sit by the fire and look at books about birds, but unless I actually study a bird, I will never know what it is. So too with the Bible. We could consider what others have written about it. But it is far better to look at the Bible itself, to discover its identifying features. We shall look at its claims and its character.

The Bible's claims

The New Testament's assessment of the Old

Perhaps the most famous verse in the Bible about its inspiration is 2 Timothy 3:16, 'All Scripture is God-breathed and is useful for teaching, rebuking, correcting, and training in righteousness.' When Timothy read these words in his letter from Paul, he knew what Paul was talking about. Memories may have come into his mind of his early childhood, when his mother used to put him on her knee, sing psalms to him, and tell him Bible stories. He would hear about the exploits of Samson, and of how David killed Goliath. Then, when he was grown up, his mother began to talk about Jesus. And she said that *everything* she'd ever taught him from Scripture pointed to Jesus. When Timothy too came to know the Lord, he saw what she meant. He saw how the Jewish Scriptures, which we call the Old Testament, had got them ready for salvation (Acts 16:1; 2 Timothy 1:5; 3:14–15). Now Paul was telling him that the whole of the Old Testament—the Scriptures that Timothy had known 'from infancy' (v.15)—came from God, and were therefore his word. We see the same message in Romans 3:2, where Paul is clearly writing about the Old Testament. This verse says that the Israelites had 'been entrusted with the very words of God'.

Paul was telling him that the whole of the Old Testament—the Scriptures that Timothy had known 'from infancy' (v.15)—came from God, and were therefore his word.

Though he is not speaking so unambiguously about the

whole of the Old Testament, Peter gives the same message. 'Above all, you must understand that no prophecy of Scripture came about by the prophet's own interpretation. For prophecy never had its origin in the will of man, but men spoke from God as they were carried along by the Holy Spirit' (2 Peter 1:20–21). The verb translated 'carried along' is used in Acts of a ship being driven along by the wind. As used here by Peter, it suggests the work of the Holy Spirit inspiring and guiding the prophets' thoughts while they wrote.

The New Testament's assessment of itself

Some of the claims made by Christ and the apostles about their own and one another's words are equally strong.

A good part of the New Testament is made up of the words of Jesus. He makes some unequivocal claims about his own words:

> For the one whom God sent speaks the words of God, for God gives the Spirit without limit . . . There is a judge for the one who rejects me and does not accept my words; that very word which I spoke will condemn him at the last day. For I did not speak of my own accord, but the Father who sent me commanded me what to say and how to say it. I know that his command leads to eternal life. So whatever I say is just what the Father has told me to say . . . Don't you believe that I am in the Father and the Father is in me? The words I say to you are not just my own. Rather, it is the Father, living in me, who is doing his work . . . He who does not love me will not obey my teaching. These words you hear are not my own; they belong to the Father who sent me.
>
> (John 3:34; 12:48–50; 14:10, 24)

16

He could not be clearer. In perfect line with his statements that all his words came from the Father was his bold assertion that 'heaven and earth will pass away, but my words will never pass away' (Matthew 24:35). Just think about that. 'In eternity, they'll still be listening to my sermons!' From anyone else, we would consider this the height of arrogance. Imagine your reaction if your pastor stood up next Sunday and thundered out such a claim! But from Jesus it makes perfect sense, for he always and only spoke the words of the living God.

What about the apostles? They had no doubt that Christ's words were God's words, for they believed that Jesus was God the Son. One particular piece of evidence for the reverence they gave to Jesus' words is in 1 Timothy 5:18. Here we see Paul writing about 'Scripture', but notice what he includes under that title: 'For the Scripture says, "Do not muzzle an ox while it is treading out the grain," and "The worker deserves his wages."' The first quotation is from Deuteronomy 25:4, so it is entirely unsurprising that Paul should refer to that as 'Scripture'. But the second quotation is *not* from the Old Testament. It is from Jesus himself. We find it recorded in Luke 10:7, but Paul is not necessarily quoting from Luke's gospel: Christ's words would have been well remembered by the apostles without their having to refer to a book, and Luke might not even have written his gospel by then. Nevertheless, for Paul to call the words 'Scripture' is effectively for him to call them 'words from the living God'.

Paul's own words make up much of the rest of the New Testament. Is he as certain that he himself is speaking God's pure word? He makes a number of relevant and intriguing statements about his own words in his first letter to the Corinthians. First we find a puzzling pair of statements in 1 Corinthians 7:10, 12: 'To the married I give this command (not I, but the Lord) . . . To the rest I say this (I, not the Lord) . . .' Could Paul be saying that some of his words are inspired by God, while others are not? No. All that Paul means is that in the case of Christians married to Christians, he knows what Jesus taught during his earthly ministry, but that in the case of Christians married to non-Christians (1 Corinthians 7:12–16), he cannot quote the earthly Jesus, but must offer an opinion 'as one who by the Lord's mercy is trustworthy' (1 Corinthians 7:25). But did Paul consider himself to be more than trustworthy? Did he think that he was inspired with the very words of God? First Corinthians 7:40 might suggest doubt, 'In my judgment, she is happier if she stays as she is—and I think that I too have the Spirit of God.' But actually, Paul was ironically criticising the self-assured certainty of the Corinthians, who were probably bragging, 'We have the Spirit of God, so we *must* be right!' He was bursting their bubble, suggesting that, just possibly, an apostle might be in touch with God's Spirit!

Where we see Paul speaking straight is in 1 Corinthians 14:37: 'If anybody thinks that he is a prophet or spiritually gifted, let him acknowledge that what I am writing to you is the Lord's command.' Unlike 1 Corinthians 7:10, where he said, 'Not I, but the Lord,' it is most *unlikely* that Paul here means that he is quoting the earthly Jesus. First, Paul expects the divine origin of his words to be *spiritually* recognised, rather than recognised from memory ('if anybody thinks he is . . . spiritually gifted, let him acknowledge . . .'). Secondly, the subject about which he is issuing God's command, which is prophecy in the local church, is not mentioned in the gospels. So if we can argue from silence, it does not seem to have caught Jesus' particular attention during his earthly ministry.

So Paul means something else: that his *own* opinion should be recognised as being of divine origin. This does not mean, of course, that Paul knew that his words would be placed alongside the Old Testament as 'Scripture', and read by God's people throughout the world for thousands of years. We can imagine him falling off his throne with shock when he arrived in paradise and was told that his letters would be Scripture! It just means that he knew his apostolic authority over the Corinthian church, and knew that God was speaking to them through him.

Peter does not make such assertions about his own words, but he does offer a comment about Paul's. And it is a comment that may well arouse our sympathies! Have you ever found Paul's words puzzling? Well, you're in good company.

> Bear in mind that our Lord's patience means salvation, just as our dear brother Paul also wrote to you with the wisdom that God gave him. He writes the same way in all his letters, speaking in them of these matters. His letters contain some things that are hard to understand, which ignorant and unstable people distort, as they do the other Scriptures, to their own destruction (2 Peter 3:15–16).

Apart from the relief we feel to know that even the great apostle Peter found that Paul was tough going in places, two things from this passage stand out. First, Peter stated that Paul had God's wisdom when he wrote. Secondly, he put Paul's letters alongside 'the other Scriptures', by which he meant the Old Testament. Peter would have believed, like every Jew in his generation, that his Scriptures were inspired by God. To put Paul's letters alongside them is to hint at the same inspiration in those letters.

We have already looked at John's gospel, and seen Christ's repeated claim that he spoke the very words of God. When we come to John's other New Testament writings, we find a contrast between his letters and the book of Revelation. In 1 John, his main appeal to the truthfulness of what he is writing is not that he is inspired, but that he is a *witness*.

> That which was from the beginning, which we have heard, which we have seen with our eyes, which we have looked at and our hands have touched—this we proclaim to you concerning the Word of life. The life appeared; we have seen it and testify to it . . . We proclaim to you what we have seen and heard . . . (1 John 1:1–3)

Nevertheless, while he is claiming to have heard with his natural ears rather than his spiritual ones, he does declare that his words are from God:

> This is the message *we have heard from him* and declare to you: God is light; in him there is no darkness at all . . . And this is what *he promised us*—even eternal life . . . And *he has given us this command*: Whoever loves God must also love his brother. (1 John 1:5; 2:25; 4:21. I have highlighted the phrases showing the divine origin of the words)

In Revelation, on the other hand, the appeal is to inspiration, pure and simple: 'The revelation of Jesus Christ, which God gave him to show his servants what must soon take place. He made it known by sending his angel to his servant John, who testifies to everything he saw—that is, the word of God and the testimony of Jesus Christ' (Revelation 1:1–2).

The Old Testament's assessment of itself

Turning from the New Testament to the Old, and starting at the beginning of our Bibles, we only have to read as far as the third verse to find a claim that we are reading words that have literally proceeded from God's mouth: 'And God said, "Let there be light," and there was light' (Genesis 1:3).

Not every book of the Old Testament claims so overtly that it contains words which come straight from God. But in the books of law and prophecy particularly, phrases like 'God says...', 'Thus says the Lord...', 'The Lord spoke...' are repeated over and over again. Whole passages, chapters long, are presented as coming straight from the mouth of God. An example is chapters thirty and thirty-one of Jeremiah, which commence in no uncertain terms:

> This is the word that came to Jeremiah *from the Lord*: 'This is what *the Lord, the God of Israel, says*: "Write in a book all the words *I have spoken to you*. The days are coming," *declares the Lord*, "when I will bring my people Israel and Judah back from captivity and restore them to the land I gave to their forefathers to possess," *says the Lord*.' These are the words *the Lord spoke* concerning Israel and Judah: 'This is what *the Lord says*: "Cries of fear are heard—terror, not peace"' (Jeremiah 30:1–5—I have highlighted all the indicators that this comes straight from God).

Throughout the rest of these two chapters, Jeremiah hammers home the message of where his prophecy comes from, using the phrase 'declares the Lord' no fewer than nineteen times. And this passage is just one example! The only verse that clearly records Jeremiah's own natural experience, rather than what he heard from God in his spirit, is the interesting little comment in Jeremiah 31:26, 'At this I awoke and looked around. My sleep had been pleasant to me.' So that's how he had been hearing from God. Perhaps he woke in a daze, unsure of where he was. It's good to know that he enjoyed the experience of hearing from God!

When we turn to Old Testament books written relatively close to the time of Christ's birth, and long after Moses, David and Isaiah had died, we find occasional passages which show us what these later writers thought of the claims of the Law and the earlier prophets.

In Nehemiah, for instance, we read of a time when the Law was read to the people. 'They stood where they were and read from the Book of the Law of the Lord their God for a quarter of the day, and spent another quarter in confession and in worshipping the Lord their God' (Nehemiah 9:3). There is no doubt that they were taking their Bible reading seriously! After the reading, the Levites prayed (Nehemiah 9:5–38). It was a long prayer, which surveyed history from creation onwards, and which showed a clear belief in every word of Genesis, Exodus, Leviticus, Numbers, Deuteronomy, Joshua and Judges. They believed that the Law was from God, and they believed that the miracles happened. The period of the kings is passed over more hastily, but then we read: 'For many years you were patient with them. By your Spirit you admonished them through your prophets' (Nehemiah 9:30). So the Levites' understanding was that the words of the prophets were the words of God, conveyed by his Spirit.

Daniel shared this attitude. He believed that Jeremiah was right when he said that his words came from God. 'I, Daniel, understood from the Scriptures, according to the word of the Lord given to Jeremiah the prophet, that the desolation of Jerusalem would last seventy years' (Daniel 9:2). Bear in mind that Daniel was a prophet himself. He was particularly well qualified to judge whether someone else's words were genuinely from God or not. When he read Jeremiah in his daily devotions, he recognised the divine handwriting, so to speak. He knew this was the real thing.

I can claim to be the prime minister. But I cannot make the claim any truer just by repeating it a lot! And it is a circular argument to say that the claims must be true 'because they're in the Bible'. Other religions have books which claim to come from their god, and yet teach very different doctrines from those found in Scripture. Is there anything beyond the Bible's own claims that confirms their truth? Yes. We can also look at its character, and its impact. First, its character.

The Bible's character

The Man at its centre

The Bible centres on Jesus Christ, and he confirmed the truth of his words by rising from the dead. 'Ah-hah,' some might say. 'You are back on a circular argument, for you only think that Jesus rose from the dead because the Bible says so!' Not true. There is other evidence for the resurrection, albeit much more indirect. First, the massive early spread of the church in the face of severe suffering is evidence that Jesus rose. We know about this spread, and about the persecution, from ancient books and other archaeology as well as from the Bible. If Christ had not risen, what shape would the disciples have been in? Would they have been the spiritual giants who would change the world upside down? Hardly! Do the doleful words, 'We had hoped that he was the one who was going to redeem Israel' (Luke 24:21), uttered by a disciple who did *not* yet know about the resurrection, sound like the recipe for a vibrant church? If the disciples had not been such giants, the church would simply never have come into existence, let alone grown so far, so fast. Similarly, the *existence* of the New Testament (as opposed to its contents) points to the resurrection. If it had not happened, if Jesus had just died a criminal's death and stayed dead, then why write? There would have been, so to speak, nothing to shout about.

But if Jesus rose from the dead, we *must* give due weight to his words. He said that the Scriptures his generation had were from God and that he himself spoke God's words in purity. So who are we to argue?

The fulfilment of its prophecy

One of the characteristics of the Bible is the number of predictions it contains. They have not all been fulfilled— yet. But the number that have should be enough to astonish anyone who believes that the Bible is of merely human origin.

Take Isaiah 44:26–45:2 for example:

24

[I am the Lord] ... who says of Jerusalem, 'It shall be inhabited,' of the towns of Judah, 'They shall be built,' and of their ruins, 'I will restore them,' who says to the watery deep, 'Be dry, and I will dry up your streams,' who says of Cyrus, 'He is my shepherd and will accomplish all that I please; he will say of Jerusalem, "Let it be rebuilt," and of the temple, "Let its foundations be laid."' This is what the Lord says to his anointed, to Cyrus whose right hand I take hold of to subdue nations before him and to strip kings of their armour, to open doors before him so that gates will not be shut: I will go before you and will level the mountains; I will break down gates of bronze and cut through bars of iron.

Isaiah prophesied during the eighth and early seventh centuries BC. In this passage, God speaks through him about a leader, Cyrus, who lived over a hundred years later. Not only did the prophecy accurately predict that Cyrus would order the rebuilding of the Jerusalem temple after the exile in Babylon (2 Chronicles 36:23), but Isaiah even knew Cyrus' name! Doesn't that suggest that we are reading *God's* word?

For another example, look at Micah 5:2, written hundreds of years before Christ's birth, and yet accurately predicting his birth-place:

But you, Bethlehem Ephrathah, though you are small among the clans of Judah, out of you will come for me one who will be ruler over Israel, whose origins are from of old, from ancient times.

The challenge of its teaching

The Bible contains truths which are unpleasant and unpalatable to writers and readers alike. Examples are the doctrines of original sin and eternal hell. If the Bible had

We cannot fail to notice the remarkable unity of the Bible's message, despite its being written over hundreds of years by many different human authors.

merely human origins, one might still find such teaching, but probably from an 'us-and-them' point of view: 'They are sinners, and will all go to hell . . . we are God's approved, and will all go to heaven'! But the facts of sin and hell are taught as universals: *everyone* has sinned; *everyone* will go to hell unless personally forgiven by God. David wrote, 'Surely I was sinful at birth, sinful from the time my mother conceived me' (Psalm 51:5). He had discovered this truth from God. Paul wrote, 'Jews and Gentiles alike are all under sin' (Romans 3:9). He was no self-righteous bigot condemning 'the other lot'!

The unity of its message

We cannot fail to notice the remarkable unity of the Bible's message, despite its being written over hundreds of years by many different human authors. Much of the Old Testament was written by Moses. He 'was educated in all the wisdom of the Egyptians' (Acts 7:22). David, author of many psalms, started life as a rural shepherd. Jeremiah, one of the Old Testament's most prolific prophets, was a priest just outside Jerusalem (Jeremiah 1:1). Matthew was a tax-collector, John a fisherman. Luke was a Gentile, Paul a Jewish intellectual. The variety of authors accounts for the variety of styles and perspectives in the Bible. But there is a unity in the message about the perfection of God, the sinfulness of mankind, the penalty

26

for wrong-doing, and the way to God and his forgiveness; and that unity points to the Bible's ultimate divine origin.

The Bible's impact

The Bible has had a profound impact on people from every culture throughout thousands of years. It has quite simply changed people's lives, and it has done so in ways that are dramatic and irreversible. Martin Luther is an outstanding example of someone whose life was quite simply revolutionised by the Bible. Living in Germany during the sixteenth century, he was a man steeped in all the teaching of the mediaeval church. He desperately wanted to be set free from the guilt he felt when he heard about God's justice, perfection and anger. So he tried every solution which the church had to offer. He performed all the good works he could think of. He tried to find peace by depending on the merit of saints who had gone to heaven before him. He spent hours in fervent confession before a priest. He even sought relief in mystic abandonment of himself to God.

But it was all useless. Only when he was appointed as a teacher of the Bible did he find the answers he had looked for. The Bible made the profound and life-changing impact on him that neither traditional church teaching nor his own heart-aching efforts had achieved. He began to deliver lectures on the Psalms and on Paul's letters to the Romans and the Galatians. And as he prepared to teach, he himself learned. Psalm 22 taught him that Christ had experienced appalling isolation from God the Father—the same desolation that Luther himself had often felt—and that Jesus had done so because of

27

Luther's own sins. Paul taught him that in suffering and dying in this way on the cross, Christ had demonstrated not only the *love* of God but also his *justice*. 'Thereupon I felt myself to be reborn and to have gone through open doors into paradise' (quoted by Roland Bainton, *Here I Stand*, p. 65).

From that moment, Luther did not look back. He taught the truth that he saw in the Bible with great fervour, and eventually at great cost to himself. But he started the Reformation of sixteenth-century Europe from which every Protestant church on earth directly or indirectly stems. And this was all because of the Bible. Might not the breath of God lie behind its words?

We also need to consider the impact that the Bible has had on our own lives. The fact that I have written this book and that you are reading it implies that the Bible has already had an effect on us. Has any other book touched us so deeply? Has any other work challenged us so profoundly, but at the same time given us such hope? Have we ever been left feeling so clearly that God has spoken to us as when we have read the Bible?

The Bible's 'contradictions'

Isn't the Bible full of contradictions? Aren't many passages mutually incompatible, so that one, at least, must be untrue, and cannot therefore be from God, the author of truth? Actually, even the potential contradictions are very few in number when compared with the enormous amount of agreement in the Bible's pages. And many of these apparent contradictions turn out to be nothing of the sort when considered carefully.

They arise because of the different human viewpoints from which various parts of the Bible are written. This applies to both historical and theological differences that look like contradictions. For a typical example of a historical 'tension', we can turn to the variation of expression between three Old Testament passages, each of which describes the occasion, in the days of Moses and of Israel's wandering in the desert, when it was agreed that spies should travel north from that wilderness to have a good look at Canaan. First, let's look at Numbers 13:1–3:

> The Lord said to Moses, 'Send some men to explore the land of Canaan, which I am giving to the Israelites. From each ancestral tribe send one of its leaders.'
> So at the Lord's command Moses sent them out from the Desert of Paran. All of them were leaders of the Israelites.

Now, let's compare Numbers 32:8, which records Moses saying, 'This is what your fathers did when I sent them from Kadesh Barnea to look over the land.'

And Deuteronomy 1:20–23 speaks of the same occasion, also in Moses' own words:

> Then I said to you, 'You have reached the hill country of the Amorites, which the Lord our God is giving us. See, the Lord your God has given you the land. Go up and take possession of it as the Lord, the God of your fathers, told you. Do not be afraid; do not be discouraged.'
> Then all of you came to me and said, 'Let us send men ahead to spy out the land for us and bring back a report about the route we are to take and the towns we will come to.'
> The idea seemed good to me; so I selected twelve of you, one man from each tribe.

At first sight, these three passages seem to contradict each other. Were the spies sent at God's command, or at Moses' command, or at the people's request? It cannot be that all the statements are true. Or can it? The following explanation is offered by John W. Haley: '. . . the true solution being that the people suggested the matter to Moses, who laid it before the Lord, and received from him an injunction to comply with the people's request.' He goes on to comment, 'Upon the shallow and delusive hypothesis that the historian's omission of an event is equivalent to a denial of that event, are founded many of the alleged ''contradictions'' of the Bible' (*Alleged Discrepancies of the Bible*, p. 350).

Now let's compare three New Testament passages to see a theological 'contradiction'. Paul and James were both inspired by the same Holy Spirit, and each wrote about the place of good deeds in the process of being justified from his own particular perspective, and, it must be added, for the particular perspective of his readers. So Paul could write, 'We maintain that a man is justified by faith apart from observing the law' (Romans 3:28) and 'by grace you have been saved, through faith . . . not by works' (Ephesians 2:8–9), while James was writing, 'You see that a person is justified by what he does and not by faith alone' (James 2:24). Admittedly these viewpoints *are* distinctly different, but the difference is one of emphasis. Both apostles were right to say what they did to their particular audiences. Paul was overcoming a reliance, in his readers, on empty ritual 'observance' of Jewish law, while James was attacking an equally perverse reliance on empty, hollow 'faith'.

There is not room in this book to look at every seeming

contradiction within the pages of Scripture. Many can be explained in terms similar to those I have just suggested. But we might not be satisfied by such explanations. So what should we do? Do we say, 'The Bible is wrong,' or do we say, 'I must be wrong. Perhaps I don't know all the relevant facts. Or maybe I can't really see the issue clearly. In this case I will assume that the Bible is right and I am wrong'? Ultimately such a decision is one of the heart. It is a value judgement, and is related to submission to the word of God. My own response is always to cast doubt on my own judgements, rather than the authenticity of the Bible.

The 'word of God' – in what sense?

Most preachers would hope, and perhaps be so bold as to claim, that their sermons are inspired. But they would not mean by such a claim that every single word they utter, from the moment they begin to preach, is precisely chosen for them and given to them by God. They would not claim that their sermons are always and entirely without error (at least not the sensible ones!). So when the Bible claims to be inspired by God, is it actually making a particularly tall claim? Is it claiming, as I and many others believe, that every word from cover to cover is God's precise sovereign choice? Or does it mean no more than the member of the congregation means when he or she encourages the preacher after the sermon with the words, 'That was really inspired this morning. Thank you so much!' Is something being read into the Bible's claims by many Christians that was not originally intended at all?

To answer such a challenging question, we must first remember the variety of ways in which the Bible expresses its claim to be from God. 'Inspired' is just one word used, and it is certainly not the commonest. Far more often, we read phrases that can only be interpreted to mean that the actual words written down are those the human author has received from God. Consider just a very few examples from the Old Testament. 'The Lord our God said to us at Horeb, ''You have stayed long enough at this mountain''' (Deuteronomy 1:6). 'I foretold the former things long ago, my mouth announced them and I made them known; then suddenly I acted, and they came to pass' (Isaiah 48:3). 'The word of the Lord came to me: ''Son of man, say to the ruler of Tyre, 'This is what the Lord says . . . ''''' (Ezekiel 28:1).

Now of course many parts of the Bible do not make any such claims for themselves. Most passages of historical narrative simply set out to record facts, without saying that the individual words in any sense come from God. And many of the psalms are actually presented the other way round, so to speak—as human words to God, rather than God's word to man. Also, in teaching passages the words are sometimes said to be of human origin. So for instance Proverbs is presented as Solomon's wisdom, and in several places refers to its contents as Solomon's own teaching, 'My son, do not forget my teaching, but keep my commands in your heart . . . ' (Proverbs 3:1). But, when Paul sums up his attitude to the *whole* Old Testament in the words, 'All Scripture is God-breathed . . . ' (2 Timothy 3:16), he is lumping together in one breath passages which make no particular claims with those that claim to be the very words of God. He does not mention a first-class category of fully inspired words and a second-class group of vaguely inspired thoughts. In effect, he was saying that words like, 'Do not forget my teaching,' from Proverbs, are as inspired—as divine in their origin—as words like, 'Son of man, say to the ruler of Tyre . . . ' in Ezekiel.

Jesus also treated the actual words used in forming the Old Testament Scriptures as being from God. 'I tell you the truth, until heaven and earth disappear, not the smallest letter, not the least stroke of a pen, will by any means disappear from the Law until everything is accomplished' (Matthew 5:18), and, 'It is easier for heaven and earth to disappear than for the least stroke of a pen to drop out of the Law' (Luke 16:17). These are strange words for Jesus to use if he only believed that the ideas behind the Old Testament were inspired by God, while the words which expressed those ideas were of merely human and necessarily fallible choice. It is much more reasonable to believe that he meant by these uncompromising warnings that every single word of Scripture was chosen by God, carried his seal of approval, and as such was inviolable and beyond human dispute.

God put his word into the minds of the Bible's human authors by the action of his Holy Spirit.

So what was the process of this unique inspiration? God put his word into the minds of the Bible's human authors by the action of his Holy Spirit. The relationship between God the Father, his Spirit, and the human author in this action of inspiration can be summed up in this way: God spoke his word *by* his Spirit *through* the author concerned. Several Bible characters used these sorts of terms. For instance, the Levites spoke to God about their forefathers in Nehemiah 9:30, 'By your Spirit you admonished them through your prophets.' Zechariah, in his Old Testament book, told of 'the words that the Lord Almighty had sent by his Spirit through the earlier prophets' (Zechariah 7:12). The apostle Peter spoke to his fellow believers about the Scripture 'which the Holy Spirit spoke long ago through the mouth of David' (Acts 1:16). In Hebrews, the writer referred to Psalm 95 as a message which God 'spoke through David' (Hebrews 4:7).

In general terms, then, the Spirit is the agent and the human author is the channel of God's word the Bible. Having said that, we have to recognise that the exact process of inspiration varied considerably from scripture to scripture.

At one extreme, God used all the human faculties required for careful research and orderly description of historical events. This is particularly obvious in historical narrative. So when we read, 'Since I myself have carefully investigated everything from the beginning, it seemed good for me also to write an orderly account' (Luke 1:3), we can picture Luke working hard at gathering his material from many sources, putting it all together carefully, and constantly reviewing what he had written. Here, the human element in the process of writing Scripture is particularly obvious, while the divine side of the operation is much more veiled.

At the other extreme, it seems that sometimes God virtually dictated his words. We see this most clearly in the biblical books of prophecy, and particularly in the letters to the seven churches recorded in Revelation chapters two and three. So we find words like these: 'To the angel of the church in Ephesus write: These are the words of him who holds the seven stars in his right hand and walks among the seven golden lampstands . . . ' (Revelation 2:1). In this case, the divine element in the process is most obvious and the human contribution is minimal. John heard the risen Christ speak certain words, heard also the command to write them down, and did so, presumably after he had 'come round' from being caught up in the Spirit. John knew these churches, however, along with their strengths and weaknesses, so his own processes of thought and real pastoral concerns were presumably not completely bypassed.

The word of God—so what?

There are enormously important consequences for all of us if the Bible is the word of God. First, it means that the Bible carries God's powerful authority. When God says, 'Let there be light,' there is light! What God says goes. Humans have a horribly large capacity for disobedience, and people are all too prone to reject God's authoritative word. But they will suffer the consequences, and ultimately, the Bible will fully succeed in achieving all of God's purposes for it, as is expressed so eloquently in Isaiah 55:10–11:

> As the rain and the snow come down from heaven, and do not return to it without watering the earth and making it bud and flourish, so that it yields seed for the sower and bread for the eater, so is my word that goes forth from my mouth: it will

35

not return to me empty, but will accomplish what I desire and achieve the purpose for which I sent it.

Anything that a person says will carry as much authority as that person has. If a policeman tells you to stop your car, you can obey or disobey as you wish, but bear in mind that the authority of the law lies behind his words! Even if the message comes through a messenger, it carries the authority of the original speaker. If you're sitting down and quietly getting on with your job, and a junior rushes in and says that the boss wants to see you in his or her office right away, whose authority is at work? The junior's, or your boss's? Would you dare to risk finding out? I'd make a bee-line for that office! So too with the Bible. If we question it, we aren't questioning the messengers but the Author. We are challenging not the authority of Moses, Jeremiah or Paul, but of God.

The fact that the Bible is the word of God means that the Bible is vibrant with God's activity. 'For the word of God is living and active. Sharper than any double-edged sword, it penetrates even to dividing soul and spirit, joints and marrow; it judges the thoughts and attitudes of the heart' (Hebrews 4:12). It is speaking *now*, because God is speaking now. When we open the pages of our Bibles, what do we think is about to happen? Do we think that we are about to examine its passive pages and paragraphs, getting to the bottom of God's deep truths as we study them? The fact is that, while God does graciously allow us to examine his truth through the pages of his word, it actively examines us! We find our lives under the spotlight. We are not gazing down the microscope at the things of God; we are under the microscope, and we find our lives exposed to the light of God's piercing, searching truth. No wonder the psalmist wrote, 'I have considered my ways and have turned my steps to your statutes' (Psalm 119:59). He did not write, 'I have considered *your* ways,' but '*my* ways'. As he read God's statutes, he found his attention drawn to his own behaviour. And he knew he had to change and bring his habits into line with God's perfect standards. We must not see ourselves as simply studying the Bible. We must recognise that we are being judged by it.

> *We are not gazing down the microscope at the things of God; we are under the microscope, and we find our lives exposed to the light of God's piercing, searching truth.*

Back to the Bible—for contemplation or discussion

1. Read Isaiah 55:10–11; Hebrews 4:12. What is God's word compared to in these passages?
2. What ideas are presented about God's word in these written 'pictures'?
3. Are you really letting the word of God do its work in your life? How could you respond more readily to what it says?

Prayer

Lord, I open up my whole life to your word, at every level. Help me not to hide any part of my being from its penetrating gaze and activity. Help me not to let pride or fear cause me to resist anything you want to say to me. I want to hear it, and say, 'Yes, Amen, Lord!'

2
Handle the Word

The Bible on our shelf is a physical thing—paper, card, glue, and the all-important ink. So it will only reach our heads and our hearts when handled by our physical senses. What handles do we have? How can we use them to get the word inside us?

Read it

This is where the whole process has to start. Sleeping with the Bible under your pillow just isn't the same! God has graciously given us his word, but we need to receive it from him by reading it.

Those of us who call ourselves charismatic or Pentecostal love God's Spirit, and constantly pray to be filled and anointed. But let's make sure that we are also filling ourselves with God's word, constantly taking in its goodness, and through it his goodness.

Read it all

God has given us the whole Bible, and it is an insult to him if we do not read it all. One day, we will all stand before God at the last judgement. Perhaps he will ask us, 'Did you read my book?' Let's make sure we can reply, 'Yes, I read it all.' Generally, more of us have read the New Testament in its entirety than the Old, and it has become more familiar ground. But none of us would take a novel out from the library, start reading it halfway through, and expect to follow the plot completely. So too with the Bible: the 'second half' which we call the New Testament is not fully understood unless it stands on the foundation of the Old.

I remember a preacher once saying, as he introduced his Bible reading, 'And if you've only brought half the Bible, you've brought the wrong half!' He was about to read from the Old Testament, and was gently chastising those who had only brought New Testaments with them. I can't say, 'If you've only read half the Bible, you've read the wrong half.' That would be going too far! But I can say, 'If you've only read half the Bible in any depth, now is the time to put the situation right.' Read it all!

There are good reasons for reading the whole Bible consistently and thoroughly. First, each part can only be fully appreciated in the context of the whole. Also, each biblical doctrine is only balanced and complete when it reflects all that the Bible has to say on that subject. We can't talk about 'what the Bible teaches on divorce' if we are only familiar with what 1 Corinthians teaches on the subject. At best, our understanding will be incomplete; at worst, it may be unbalanced or distorted. We can see the danger of selective reading of the Bible by looking at the cults. There *are* verses which, when taken in isolation, support the view of Jesus that is held by Jehovah's Witnesses (they deny that he is God the Son). By taking certain verses as their proof-texts, and ignoring or mistranslating many others, these people build a case for their version of Jesus. But when Scripture is taken *as a whole* then its complete truth shines out, and falsehood is avoided.

> *When Scripture is taken* as a whole *then its complete truth shines out, and falsehood is avoided.*

To make sure we read it all, we need to read systematically. All serious readers of the Bible use some sort of system, at least some of the time. Just 'dipping' into the pages of the Bible at random cannot have long-term value, though it may well be useful on occasions. We may choose to dip into magazines and newspapers, but we must take the Bible more seriously. We have to recognise that its parts relate to each other far more intimately and significantly than do the articles in a newspaper!

So how can we introduce some degree of system to our Bible reading? There are many ways. We can follow a plan to read the Bible in a year. Simple plans can be obtained at Christian bookshops. Also, several editions of Bibles in different versions have such plans included in their introductory or concluding pages. For instance, *The Every Day Devotional Bible* (New International Version), published by Hodder and Stoughton, includes both a one-year Bible reading plan and excerpted notes from *Every Day with Jesus. The One Year Bible*, using the Living Bible version (a 'thought-for-thought' translation), is published by Kingsway. It has 365 daily readings of balanced length using the Bible order, but taking each day a passage from the Old Testament, the New Testament, the Psalms and Proverbs. With such Bibles and plans, even if we don't get through the whole lot in a single year, we are provided with an order in which to devour every morsel of God's word.

We can of course simply read our normal Bibles from start to finish, but most of us get bogged down somewhere in Leviticus, and need a break from the skin diseases and the mildew to pursue some teaching from the New Testament. So reading successive Old Testament and New Testament books alternately is useful—Genesis, Matthew, Exodus, Mark, and so on.

The order of our standard Bibles is not exactly chronological. Note for instance how the books of Ezra and Nehemiah come a long way before the end of the Old Testament, even though they record events that occurred right at the close of the Old Testament era. However, it is possible to buy a 'chronological' Bible, which goes through biblical events in the order in which they happened, and then read it from start to finish. The sort of historical overview we gain by reading the Bible in chronological order is excellent for getting a 'broad sweep' of biblical events. *The Daily Bible* (New International Version), published by Harvest House Publishers, is set out in chronological order *and* designed to be read in its entirety in one year.

Lastly, using Bible notes can be very helpful in giving us a systematic approach to God's word, as well as providing us with some comment on what passages mean. Most popular in my church bookshop is *Every Day with Jesus*, published by CWR. This takes related themes for Bible study. Scripture Union publish three sets of notes: *Encounter with God* is systematic and in-depth in its approach; *Daily Bread* goes through Bible passages in consecutive order (as they appear in our standard Bibles) and is more basic in its comments; *Alive to God* takes different themes from an imaginative angle. *Encounter with God* also contains a list of passages for daily reading that takes you through the Bible in a year. The recommended readings with the notes cover the whole Bible in four to six years. It's good to spend some time browsing in your local Christian bookshop, to see precisely what is available, and what suits you most. Similar notes are also published for children.

If we do not read all the Bible, we are bound to linger on favourite portions and ignore the difficult, unpleasant, or boring parts, and let's face it: we do find some parts of the Bible boring! Please don't think that in saying this I am speaking against the Bible. I recognise that the fault lies not in God's perfect word but in us, imperfect readers that we are. If we are honest with ourselves, we will recognise that there are portions of God's word which we tend to ignore. Many of us need to work hard at improving our knowledge and understanding of these sections.

The hard work necessary to become familiar with the whole Bible calls for the basic conviction, set out in the last chapter, that the whole Bible is God's word. Yes, the *whole* Bible, including even 1 Chronicles 3! If you don't know why I have just included an exclamation mark, go right now and read 1 Chronicles 3. I remember a class discussion in which I took part when I was a student at Bible college. We were talking about whether preaching was only valid when the preacher felt that he or she had been 'given' a particular message by the Spirit for that particular time (often called a *rhema* word), or whether systematic preaching of 'the whole counsel of God' (Acts 20:27, New King James Version) could also be valid. I was strongly backing the latter view, and, picking up my Bible, said that I should be able to open my Bible at random and preach from *any* verse my finger landed on, simply because it was all God's word. Now, God certainly has a sense of humour, because of course I opened my Bible randomly to make my point, and ended up looking at a verse just like 1 Chronicles 3:11 ('Jehoram his son, Ahaziah his son, Joash his son')! After feeling silly for a moment, I realised that God had made his point more forcibly than I could have, for of course such a verse *is* his word, *is* valuable, and *must* be listened to. I must admit that I have yet to preach from it (or hear anyone else do so, for that matter!). If I ever do so, I'll point out the tremendous importance that the Jews, returning from years of dreadful exile in Babylon, attached to their family trees—of which 1 Chronicles 3:11 is a part. If they could show that Abraham was their direct ancestor, they proved that they were the real thing—true Jews. And I would talk about the way that we are only real Christians if we can trace our spiritual family tree directly to God the Father through the Lord Jesus Christ. You see? It all has something to say.

Read it often

Jesus taught us to pray, 'Give us today our daily bread' (Matthew 6:11). If he wants us to pray this, it is certainly his will to grant it. And we don't have to be experts to realise that he means more than just bread. At the very least, he means food in general! And he probably refers to all the resources at our heavenly Father's disposal which we need in order to live active and effective lives for him here on earth.

Jesus quoted Deuteronomy 8:3 when the devil tempted him to turn rocks into loaves: 'Man does not live on bread alone, but on every word that comes from the mouth of God' (Matthew 4:4). So if God wants to give us the regular physical resources we need to live for him, he certainly also wants to give us the spiritual ones, especially his word.

So, let's feed constantly on his word, not just by listening to sermons once a week—no one can stay healthy on one meal a week, however delicious it might be—but by reading the Bible frequently. Let's make Bible reading a regular, preferably a daily routine. We are not bound by rigid rules on this point. We won't lose our salvation if we go for one day without reading God's word. But if we miss it out for any length of time, our spiritual lives will become thin and weak, like a plant that tries to grow without sufficient light.

Reading the Bible frequently will confirm the practice as a habit, and old habits—even good habits—die hard. In the case of the Bible, to misquote the famous proverb, familiarity does *not* breed contempt! Let's make it a firm and well-established habit, part of our daily pattern of life, as regular (though not as mindless!) as cleaning our teeth.

Read it repeatedly

If we add together the last two points, 'read it all' and 'read it often', we will find that we are reading Bible passages repeatedly. A passage that we last read some weeks, months or years ago comes up once more for study. Do we say, 'Oh, I've already read this passage. I've already heard what God has to say to me through this one. There's no point in reading it again'? No! Would you, if ravenously hungry and offered fish and chips, say,

'Well, thanks, but I've actually had fish and chips before in my life. Offer me something else'? Of course not! You would fall on the food, not caring so much what it was, but just grateful to have something to eat. So too with the Bible. We need to be fed, whether or not we've actually had that particular food before.

We need to read passages over and over again. Unlike elephants we forget and we need reminding. Our faith in God's particular promises may need recharging. Our obedience to his commands may need refocusing. But there's more to it than that. We find, as we read the same passages over and over again, that two things happen to our understanding.

First, we discover that verses or passages which have never previously made sense at last fall into place. We may have read a portion over and over before. It perhaps made a little sense, but still left us largely puzzled. Now we read it once again, and this time it's as if a light switch has been flicked on. Quite suddenly, where things were obscure, all is light. Why is this?

It is because our understanding of any individual passage depends partly on our understanding of the rest of the Bible, and since we last read that passage, our knowledge of the rest has grown. We are at last able to relate this obscure passage to another which we did not know when we read it before, but which now throws light on the problem. Also, we understand a Bible passage in the context of our whole lives, our overall experience. And since we last read a passage, our experience has grown. Perhaps we have now been through what is being described. So it makes more sense. It's just like reading a well-written novel. Good writers don't give everything away at once. The plot takes time to unfold. As it does, earlier bits which we didn't clearly follow begin to make more sense. And many of us can't resist the temptation to go back and read those bits again, with silent cries of, 'Ah hah, I see now!'

A second result of rereading Scripture is that portions which have always made perfect sense take on a whole new significance. The significance that any biblical passage has for us depends not only on its objective meaning, but on what we're going through at the time we read it. It 'speaks to us where we're at'. We may have fully understood a passage on grief, but when we're actually going through a process of bereavement and grief, that same passage, already long understood, will overflow with new personal significance.

Read it fast, read it slow

The speed at which we read a portion of Scripture will affect what we receive from it. If we read several chapters or even books in one sitting, reading fast, we may miss detail, but we will get a most helpful overview, possibly seeing connections that would otherwise have escaped us. On the other hand, if we read slowly and carefully, even perhaps just a few verses, God has maximum opportunity to open up the full meaning and impact to us. I would recommend doing both, sometimes going for the 'big picture' without concentrating on detail, and at other times homing in on just a few words.

Read different versions

I think it is wise to use just one translation of the Bible for our main reading and study, largely because it is easier to

memorise that way. However, it is refreshing and reveal-
ing to turn occasionally to other versions. Further aspects
of God's word thus come our way, as we see biblical truth
put slightly differently. For the linguists among us, it may
also prove helpful to read the Bible in the different
languages that we know, for the same reason.

I am often asked which version of the Bible I think is
best. I admit there are differences between the versions,
but compared with what they have in common (after all,
they are all translating the same Bible) the differences are
small. It is more important to have a version that we are
comfortable with than to have the 'right' version. Then we
can get to use it a lot, know it well, and memorise sections
within it. I use the New International Version for everyday
reading and study. My second port of call, for immediate
comparison, is the New King James Version. However,
when I first became a Christian I read the Good News
Bible almost exclusively and found it excellent at that
stage, as is the Living Bible. These are looser and simpler
translations, offering an easier vocabulary.

Read it with pen in hand

This may sound unimportant, but I recommend it strongly.
Let's write as we read! So many things occur to me while I
am reading that are worth noting down (at least, I think they
are!). They may be formal notes about what a verse means,
or they may be informal and personal comments, or prayers.
Now, I at least find that I have to write them down then and
there. If I say that I'll look for a pen later, when I've finished
my reading, I forget completely, or forget precisely what I
was going to write down, or in some other way lose the fresh
impact before it is committed to paper.

The first thing we'll probably want to use our pens for is underlining or highlighting words and phrases. Some people disapprove of underlining, saying that to do so is to make value judgements that some verses are more important than others. Well, they are! At least, they are more important to us *at that time*. There is no harm in underlining a verse, as long as we don't then ignore the surrounding verses. An underlined verse will stand out from the page (important if we are looking for it quickly), and will remind us next time we come to it that it had particular significance to us on a previous reading.

You may also want to make cross references. In other words, to write in the reference to a verse elsewhere in the Bible that relates in some way to the one you are reading (useful for later comparisons). My main study Bible is a cross-reference Bible, but it is also full of my own cross-references, quite apart from the 'official' ones.

Also, you may want to make notes, as I do. Some publishers produce wide-margin Bibles to allow for this. At Kensington Temple, where I am one of the ministers, we often have some of the best preachers in the world coming to visit and preach. Sometimes I get a chance to sneak a look at their Bibles when these are lying open on the lectern. The preachers' Bibles are usually packed full of hand-written comments in the margins, sometimes so dense they are hardly legible! Yet I know that each of those comments marks an encounter between God's word and that preacher. I'm happy to be following their example.

On the other hand, some people, my wife included, prefer to keep a separate note book for this purpose. They want to know that when they next turn to a passage which they have previously made notes about, they will not immediately be swayed in their thinking by what they wrote last time, but will approach the passage freshly, with their previous comments hidden away out of sight. Obviously, there are advantages and disadvantages to both systems. Experiment and find out what suits you best.

> *We need to prioritise Bible reading in our lives. Sometimes we can be so busy reading books about the Bible that we neglect reading the Bible itself.*

We need to prioritise Bible reading in our lives. Sometimes we can be so busy reading books *about* the Bible that we neglect reading the Bible itself. I can remember a time fairly early on in my Christian life when I was reading so many Christian books, to the neglect of Bible reading, that I had to put a ban for a year or so on my reading any Christian books other than the Bible. It did me a lot of good to focus on the Bible alone for that period. We all need to ask ourselves, 'Am I getting my reading priorities right—at the moment?' Even reading this book could be a diversion: dare I ask you whether you should at this moment be reading this book or reading the Bible itself . . . ?

Write it

Following on naturally from my encouragement to read the Bible with pen in hand is the next physical handle: to write it out. Try to make opportunities for writing verses out in full. For those of us who like to put a reference at the bottom of the page when we send people a letter or card, we can take time to write out the verse rather than simply giving the reference (apart from anything else, they're more likely to read it if they don't have to look it up!). If you are giving someone a Bible, and writing a message inside the cover, do the same thing. For the preachers and leaders among us, when we are writing out notes during preparation for sermons or discussions, let's write out relevant scriptures in full.

Some people find it helpful to keep written verses on a card-index system. This can be arranged according to different themes perhaps, so that relevant scriptures on comfort, assurance, holiness, etc. can be found.

There are three particular reasons why it is helpful to write scriptures out. One is that the process helps verses to have a greater impact on us than if we only read them. It takes longer to write a verse than to read it, and we *have* to notice every word, while during normal reading our eyes actually scan lines, not distinctly taking in every single word. A second related reason is that writing verses out in full helps us to memorise them. And thirdly, we can keep that written verse before our eyes, perhaps hanging on the wall of the kitchen, tucked in our glasses-case or taped to the dashboard of the car (only to be read when the vehicle is stationary!). Moses wrote surprising words when he encouraged the Israelites to find ways of keeping the commandments vividly before their eyes: 'Tie them as symbols on your hands and bind them on your foreheads. Write them on the door-frames of your houses and on your gates' (Deuteronomy 6:8–9). Spiritual tattoos and spiritual graffiti! What might modern equivalents be? When visiting Sao Paulo, a city in Brazil, I noticed that many young Christians wore tee-shirts emblazoned with God's word. There are innumerable ways of keeping the truth in front of our eyes. Let's find useful ways to do so.

Listen to it

These days, the Bible is available on audio and even video cassette tapes. I often listen to Scripture in the car. My family listens together to a dramatised version, more suitable for children. A friend at church wanders round with his personal stereo pumping in the Bible. By all these means the ear-gate is opened to Scripture as well as the eye-gate, and time is utilised when *reading* the Bible would be impractical or even impossible. One good discipline about listening to the Bible on cassette tape is that you have to listen to it at its speed, rather than yours. So you don't race on ahead or jump about all the time, but listen right through a book from beginning to end. You generally cover far more of the Bible this way than you do by giving the same length of time to reading. Mind you, I still like to switch off the tape every now and then and really think about what I'm listening to.

Speak and sing it

Psalm 119 is the most extended piece of writing in the Bible expressing right heart attitudes towards the word of God. I can't help noticing that there, where attitudes of the *heart* are being emphasised, we also find that the word of God is on the psalmist's *lips*. Look for instance at verse 13: 'With my lips I recount all the laws that come from your mouth.' Why did the psalmist so often express God's word out loud? It is not that easy to answer such a question from the psalm itself, for the psalmist's inspired thoughts, like a butterfly moving from bloom to bloom, fly from one aspect to another of his relationship with God's word, without ever staying long enough to develop his thought at length. However, two of these verses supply a glimpse into his thinking.

First, he encouraged himself: 'Your decrees are the theme of my song wherever I lodge' (Psalm 119:54). I love the thought of this psalmist settling down for the night wherever life's pilgrimage had taken him, perhaps one night in a luxury five-star inn and the next in the squalor of an outhouse, and always finding encouragement through the truths he could sing. Whatever the circumstances, even if perhaps he found himself sleeping in a cowshed, God's word on his lips kept his heart buoyant.

What connects our lips with our hearts (spiritually, I mean!)? Jesus told us that 'out of the overflow of the heart the mouth speaks' (Matthew 12:34). This means that what is inside our hearts will determine what comes out of our mouths in speech and song. If we believe what we read, we'll be declaring it! But it is also true that what comes out of our mouths affects what is in our hearts. It's as if what we actually say or sing drives truths deeper into our spirits and makes them permanent. I wonder how many of us have noticed, as I often have, that a thought or a feeling, once expressed, has greater clarity and certainty than when it was just an idea. The same principle holds true for the word of God. We will

We will believe it all the more firmly when we are declaring it.

believe it all the more firmly when we are declaring it. God wants his word on our lips.

Secondly, the psalmist shared with others: 'I will speak of your statutes before kings and will not be put to shame' (Psalm 119:46). We see the psalmist having the honour of an audience with the king. He knows full well what the most important words are that he can offer in such a situation. No doubt he prays fervently the night before that the king will bring up the subject of God's word—and that he won't mess up the glorious opportunity to speak up for God in that situation. He is determined not to be ashamed, either of God's word, or of his own ignorance of the word, or anything else. He will hold his head up high and declare the uncompromising decrees of the Lord.

Like the psalmist, we need to take every opportunity to witness to non-Christians and to teach and encourage other believers. 'Let the word of Christ dwell in you richly as you teach and admonish one another with all wisdom, and as you sing psalms, hymns and spiritual songs with gratitude in your hearts to God' (Colossians 3:16).

We can also note here 1 Timothy 4:13: 'Devote yourself to the public reading of Scripture.' The original Greek only says 'reading', not 'public reading' (see the Authorised Version for a more literal translation), but it is clear from the context that public ministry was in Paul's mind, rather than Timothy's own private reading. In the days when the New Testament was being written, people did not have the access to the Bible that we enjoy today in many countries. Then, the various books and letters were contained on heavy, expensive scrolls, sometimes made of parchment (2 Timothy 4:13), not at all the sort of thing that the average household would have on its shelves! Also, a fair proportion of the population would be unable to read, so hearing the Scriptures publicly read on the Lord's day might be the only access to God's word that many Christians enjoyed.

Today, things are different. More people are able to read, and most of us probably own several Bibles. So it might be argued that Paul's directive no longer carries the same force. However, I know from experience the sheer impact that the public reading of extended passages of Scripture has had on classes I have taught in Bible school.

So let's read the Bible aloud in our homes with our families; in our housegroups before Bible-study discussions; in our pulpits before preaching; in our classes before teaching.

As well as quoting it verbatim, God wants us to talk *about* his word. 'These commandments that I give you today are to be upon your hearts. Impress them on your children. Talk about them when you sit at home and when you walk along the road, when you lie down and when you get up' (Deuteronomy 6:6–7). Discuss God's word, at home and with friends; after church on Sunday; on the way home and over lunch. Don't simply dismiss the message from your minds. Talk about it.

Other people will be blessed when they hear the word of God on our lips. We may not all be Bible teachers or expert preachers. But we can all be mouth-pieces of the living God. What a privilege! The Scriptures themselves, handled sensitively and appropriately, will be a blessing to others when we share them.

Back to the Bible—for contemplation or discussion

1. Read Deuteronomy 6:6–9. What were the Israelites told to do with God's commands?
2. Why do you think they were told to do these things?
3. What practical steps can you take in your situation to achieve the same effects, at home, at work, at college, or while travelling?

Prayer

Father, thank you for the examples of your people in the Bible, who showed their commitment to your words by expressing them with lips and pen. I make a commitment to do the same; to share your word, to talk about your word, and to express what is true to your word.

3
Three Vital Spiritual Principles

Unlike studying an advanced science text-book, handling the Bible is *not* just a mental process. It is a *spiritual* process, involving three vital spiritual principles: asking the help of the Holy Spirit; avoiding the interference of our spiritual enemy; and allowing the word to reach our spirits.

Asking the help of the Holy Spirit

Before I became a Christian, the Bible meant little or nothing to me. As a child, I was once given a King James Version. Some older friends, very cultured, immediately enthused about the beautiful old English in it. They encouraged me to look at the words of dedication to King James at the beginning of the volume. I opened it at the appropriate page and read:

> Great and manifold were the blessings, most dread Sovereign, which Almighty God, the Father of all mercies, bestowed upon us the people of *England*, when first he sent Your Majesty's Royal Person to rule and reign over us. For whereas it was the expectation of many, who wished not well our *Sion*, that, upon the setting of that bright *Occidental*

57

Star, Queen *Elizabeth*, of most happy memory, some thick and palpable clouds of darkness . . .

Are you following this? I didn't! And that was about the last interest I took in the Bible until my conversion. Yet on the evening I was saved and the Holy Spirit came into my life, I read great chunks of Romans and 1 Corinthians. I didn't notice any problem passages (I've since learned how to find difficulties!). I seemed to understand every word. Before, I had had no interest and no understanding. Now I had both. What was the difference? It was the Holy Spirit in my heart.

We have already looked at the Bible's unambiguous claims to be the word of God, inspired by the Holy Spirit. And just as the Holy Spirit inspired the *writers*, so too we *readers* need his help to make sense of the Bible. It is not true that from our conversion on we will never make any mistakes in trying to understand the Bible. But we do recognise that God's direct input aids our reading processes. Someone shut off from the guidance of the Spirit may well understand the actual words of a biblical passage, but will not receive the lesson that passage is designed to teach.

As we have seen earlier, the work of the Spirit which lies behind the writing of the Bible is made clear in passages such as 2 Timothy 3:16 and 2 Peter 1:20–21. And in the same way there are other passages where we can see the work of the Spirit behind reading the Bible. Three particular instances in Paul's letters deserve our attention.

'Take . . . the sword of the Spirit, which is the word of God' (Ephesians 6:17). The sword here is the last piece of armour in Paul's well-known list, but this entry is not the same as the others. Whereas phrases like, 'the breastplate of righteousness' and 'the shield of faith' mean 'the breastplate *which is* righteousness' and 'the shield *which is* faith', 'the sword of the Spirit' does not mean 'the sword *which is* the Spirit'. No, Paul goes on to identify the sword as the word of God. In this case, 'of the Spirit' means '*belonging to* the Spirit'. The Spirit is the only one who can truly handle that sword—the word—because he owns it. He alone has the power and wisdom to take it and apply it where it is needed. As Paul writes elsewhere, 'No-one knows the thoughts of God except the Spirit of God' (1 Corinthians 2:11). So when we read Paul's instruction to handle the word of truth correctly (2 Timothy 2:15), we must be careful to realise that only the Holy Spirit can handle the word of God perfectly. Think of a glove, lying by itself. It can do nothing at all unless filled and moved by a hand within. It cannot even move, let alone pick something up and use it. It would just lie there, flat, useless and lifeless. But with a hand inside, the glove could pick up a sword. The glove would be physically touching the sword, but the hand would enable and direct every movement. We are like that glove, and the Holy Spirit is like the hand within which fills and moves the glove. We handle the word; the Spirit makes this possible.

> *We handle the word; the Spirit makes this possible.*

'The man without the Spirit does not accept the things that come from the Spirit of God, for they are foolishness to him, and he cannot understand them, because they are spiritually discerned' (1 Corinthians 2:14). Paul has just described how his message has not been put together by

59

mere human wisdom but has been revealed by the Spirit. He has gone on to show that only the Holy Spirit has access to God's thoughts—the very subject matter of the Bible itself. So it is the Spirit alone who can communicate these divine thoughts to the human heart, giving under-standing—and the words to express that understanding. Now Paul declares that a person relying on natural human intelligence, without the help of the Spirit, will not under-stand or accept such revelation. We can have an amazing intelligence and a superb education, but unless our hearts are taught by the Spirit, we will not hear God speaking through the pages of Scripture. We must constantly ask the Holy Spirit to fill our lives and soften our hearts so that he can guide us 'into all truth' (John 16:13).

> But their minds were made dull, for to this day the same veil remains when the old covenant is read. It has not been removed, because only in Christ is it taken away. Even to this day when Moses is read, a veil covers their hearts. But whenever anyone turns to the Lord, the veil is taken away. Now the Lord is the Spirit, and where the Spirit of the Lord is, there is freedom (2 Corinthians 3:14–17).

Here Paul makes it abundantly clear that God only enables people to understand the Old Testament when they turn to Christ. And the same principle applies to the New Testa-ment. We see an instance of Jesus granting this kind of understanding in Luke 24:45: 'Then he opened their minds so that they could understand the Scriptures.' What Jesus did in his disciples' presence on that occasion he now does by his Spirit.

How do we receive this help? We ask: 'Teach me your decrees' (Psalm 119:12). This is a constant prayer of the psalmist. We find it repeated constantly throughout this longest of psalms. At first sight this might seem an unnecessary prayer, for the psalmist has a brain in his head, and the decrees in his hand, so surely all he has to do is read, rather than pray. However, he does *not* feel self-sufficient. He recognises his absolute dependence on God to get those decrees off the page and into his head and heart. We too are to approach the Bible prayerfully, praising God for his word, asking him to grant us his Spirit to open us to his word, asking to be fed, and offering to give ourselves to his teaching.

Praise God that this help of the Holy Spirit *is* available to us all when we ask. The Spirit is still active today and speaking through the Scriptures. God hasn't changed. The Spirit who inspired the words of the Bible thousands of years ago is now wanting to speak to us, through those same words. When he inspired the Scriptures, he had every future generation of readers in mind, including us!

The human authors, of course, did not even know that we would exist. Take Paul as an example. We can imagine him dictating the letter we call 1 Corinthians. When he was looking over the shoulder of his secretary, checking that the words were his choice and would speak directly to the needs of the Cor-inthians, he did not have *us* in mind. His attention was focused, naturally, on the Corinthians, for whom he had a deep pastoral love, and on their many problems,

> *But as Paul was looking over his secretary's shoulder, the Holy Spirit was looking over Paul's shoulder, making sure that the words were also* his *choice, and would speak directly to us.*

61

for which he felt he had an answer from God. But as Paul was looking over his secretary's shoulder, the Holy Spirit was looking over Paul's shoulder, making sure that the words were also *his* choice, and would speak directly to us as well as to the Corinthians.

God has formed an intimate relationship between the work of his Spirit and his word. We would do well to maintain that relationship. Unfortunately, we often get off balance. Some of us are 'word people'; we love to engross ourselves in Bible study, but are disconcerted by manifestations of the Spirit. Others of us are 'Spirit people', who delight to see signs of the Spirit moving but find the Bible tedious or even irrelevant. We need to ask ourselves which side we fall. Do we prefer the 'worship time' or the preaching time in our regular Sunday church meetings? Our answer to this question may show up any imbalance in us.

God wants us to maintain a balance between Spirit and word. His Spirit is like water, and his word like bread. If we gorge ourselves on the word, but neglect the Spirit, we will be well fed, perhaps even fat, but we will be as dry as dust and will die of thirst. On the other hand, if we drink deeply of the Spirit, but fail to feed on the word, we will be floating and swimming in the water of the Spirit, but we will be starving to death. Let's get the balance right.

Avoiding the interference of our spiritual enemy

What comes into your mind when you hear the expression 'spiritual warfare'? Do you only connect the phrase with an aggressive mode of prayer—shouting at the devil? Or do you understand what is going on behind the scenes when you are witnessing to an unbeliever, worshipping God, playing your part in a good Christian marriage, or even shopping for someone who is ill? These are all aspects of spiritual warfare—when Satan's hosts and strategies are being challenged in Christ's name by believers. A biography of evangelist Reinhard Bonnke is called *Plundering Hell*. That clearly illustrates the connection between evangelism and spiritual conflict. And the connection between worship and the spiritual fight comes out in the Bible itself. 'From the lips of children and infants you have ordained praise because of your enemies, to silence the foe and the avenger' (Psalm 8:2). Jesus quoted this when children in Jerusalem were shouting his praise (Matthew 21:16). In the same way, we need to realise that every time we open and read the Bible, we take part in an act of spiritual aggression. We are doing something that Satan's forces hate and will try to stop.

We need to realise that every time we open and read the Bible, we take part in an act of spiritual aggression.

Jesus tells us that Satan is 'the father of lies' (John 8:44). We must appreciate that every time anyone reads the Bible, our spiritual enemy will try to get that person to *misinterpret* it. In fact, the Bible is probably the most misinterpreted and misunderstood book ever written. An obvious example of this is how it is misused by cults and teachers of false religions. The work of the devil lies behind such twisting of the truth. He is of course helped by mankind's fallen nature, which has left people with a natural tendency towards sinful, false thinking. When

63

Romans 1:18 speaks of 'men who suppress the truth by their wickedness', it has mankind in general in view, not just a particularly malicious class of evildoer.

Another similar satanic strategy is to blind people to the truth that would set them free. Ephesians 4:18 shows us that people who are far from God are 'darkened in their understanding'. In 2 Corinthians 4:4, Paul lays the blame squarely at the devil's door: 'The god of this age has blinded the minds of unbelievers, so that they cannot see the light of the gospel of the glory of Christ, who is the image of God.'

Now one thing we can be sure of about the devil is that he is unimaginative; he has been using the same old temptations since Eden. Mind you, if we weren't so temptable in the same old areas, he wouldn't be so successful! We need to be aware that what he has used successfully with unbelievers, he will try with believers. Just look at his tactic of lying. It has worked with non-Christians, so he'll try it on Christians: 'For false Christs and false prophets will appear and perform great signs and miracles to deceive even the elect—if that were possible' (Matthew 24:24).

Thus it is not surprising to find prayers in the Bible along the lines of, 'Open my eyes to see and understand your word.' For instance, we find the psalmist praying, 'Open my eyes that I may see wonderful things in your law' (Psalm 119:18). Given his way, the devil would make all Bible reading dull and boring, especially such books as Leviticus and Deuteronomy (the sort of books that Psalm 119 would have primarily in mind), or even Psalm 119 itself, which we have to admit is repetitive and potentially soporific! But God in his grace will answer our prayer to open us up to his word, not just so that we can concentrate when we read (sometimes enough of a miracle in itself!), but so that we can see the wonder of what is written.

We need to pray actively against the lying, blinding influences of the enemy. When I have taught this lesson in Bible schools in different countries, I have found that some students recognise that they are harassed spiritually in this area, and that they need prayer. I remember one woman who had grown up in an Eastern religion telling me that she felt overcome by a great sleepiness whenever she tried to read the Bible. I also remember another person joyfully telling me of the difference she had felt since being prayed for in this area. Don't be fooled into blaming demons, however, if in fact you are simply being disorganised or lazy, have wrong priorities or are over-tired.

Allowing the word to reach our spirits

To hear God through the pages of the Bible, we do not need to be intelligent—we need a right spirit, a right heart attitude. Psalm 119 is all about heart attitudes to God's word. As well as mentioning specific heart responses, some of which we shall consider in a few moments, we hear the psalmist praying more generally: 'Turn my heart towards your statutes and not towards selfish gain' (verse 36), and declaring, 'My heart is set on keeping your decrees to the very end' (verse 112). What did he mean by his 'heart'? An Old Testament Israelite would have meant the centre of his being, which governed all his actions. He would not be thinking of mere emotion—his heart as opposed to his head—but would include what we think of as the mind and will. In contrast, he thought of his *emotional* centre as being in his guts! But he would mean something far deeper than mere intelligence or rational thought. His use of the words 'heart' and 'spirit' would in fact be very close to our own usage of 'spirit'. The two terms are placed together in Psalm 51:17: 'The sacrifices of God are a broken spirit; a broken and contrite heart, O God, you will not despise.'

So what specific responses of the heart—of the spirit—do we see in this psalm?

A heart that submits

This response of obedience receives the most attention in Psalm 119. We find prayers which beg, 'Do good to your servant and I will live; I will obey your word' (verse 17), and promises remembered, 'I have taken an oath and confirmed it, that I will follow your righteous laws' (verse 106). His response to God's word arises primarily from his relationship with God himself, whom he holds in awe—an awe which demands obedience. He holds what God says in higher esteem and honour than what anyone else says. Even if other people stand over him with a whip, he will still pay more attention to what God is saying than to what they are shouting. 'Rulers persecute me without cause, but my heart trembles at your word' (verse 161). If we were being beaten up, whose words would make us tremble? Possibly those of our oppressors. But not so with the psalmist. He trembles at God's word. His obedience is encouraged by his knowledge that God sees everything he does: 'I obey your precepts and your statutes, for all my ways are known to you' (verse 168).

The psalmist is completely honest and confesses the same perplexing mixture of obedience and disobedience in his life that we know too well in our own. He claims with one breath, '. . . I keep your statutes' (verse 22), yet cries in another, 'Oh, that my ways were steadfast in obeying your decrees!' (verse 5).

Are we challenged by the psalmist's attitude? Do we share his submissiveness? Do we cry out to God to change those areas of our lives where we hear but do not obey? Jesus said, 'Everyone who hears these words of mine and does not put them into practice is like a foolish man who built his house on sand' (Matthew 7:26). James uses a different analogy to draw the same conclusion, 'Do not merely listen to the word, and so deceive yourselves. Do what it says. Anyone who listens to the word but does not do what it says is like a man who looks at his face in a mirror and, after looking at himself, goes away and immediately forgets what he looks like' (James 1:22–24).

Obedience is closely connected to understanding. If someone tells me, in Japanese, to cross the road, he will be sorely frustrated, not by my disobedience, but by my total ignorance of the language. So it is with God's commands. We have to understand them to obey them. 'Give me understanding, and I will keep your law and obey it with all my heart' (Psalm 119:34).

But with the Bible, it works the other way, too. We put ourselves in a better position to understand God's word if we are trying to obey it. 'I have more understanding than the elders, for I obey your precepts' (Psalm 119:100). I love to think of this psalmist, who was obviously a young man (see verse 8), sitting at the back of the meeting,

We put ourselves in a better position to understand God's word if we are trying to obey it.

listening to the 'great teachers' at the front, and thinking to himself, '*That* isn't what that passage means! I can make more sense of this subject than *he* can!' I can imagine him beginning to realise that the particular teachers who lacked understanding were the same ones whose actions fell short of the mark; the ones whose lives had the hint of hypocrisy. And once he'd realised that, he will have seen that his greater understanding arose because he was prepared to put what God said into action.

The more we are prepared to put God's word into practice in our lives, the more sense it will make to us. 'To the Jews who had believed him, Jesus said, "If you hold to my teaching, you are really my disciples. Then you shall know the truth, and the truth will set you free"' (John 8:31–32). Notice the progression of thought here. Knowledge of the truth follows from holding to Christ's teaching which means obeying it submissively.

So, more understanding leads to more obedience, and more obedience leads to more understanding. We talk about 'vicious circles'. But what about 'virtuous spirals'? Well, we have one here. Think of a spiral staircase. As we go round it, so too we find ourselves climbing up it. Once we have, so to speak, reached our starting point by completing a full revolution, we actually find ourselves one floor up. That is what happens on the spiral of understanding and obedience. Let us say that the starting point is our attempt at obedience. We may be somewhat faulty, but God sees our attempts, and graciously increases our understanding. So we climb from our starting point to understanding. Then our richer understanding leads to a greater obedience. We are back at obedience now—but we are one floor up—our obedience is greater than it was. Now as we climb the second storey, we are improving in our understanding again through the greater obedience we now have.

On the other hand, there is a vicious circle of disobedience and failure to understand. Disobedience grieves the Holy Spirit and hardens the human heart, both of which block a right understanding of the Scriptures. So let's make absolutely sure that we're willing to submit to God's word—that we're going up the spiral staircase, not down.

A heart full of faith

The psalmist sees trust as vital. First it enables him to use the truth of God's word to fight off verbal attack: 'Then I will answer the one who taunts me, for I trust in your word' (verse 42). God's word can only be used if it is trusted. If Jesus had not really believed Deuteronomy, what defence would it have been against Satan's taunts in the wilderness? But Jesus *did* believe, and was able to respond, 'It is written . . . ' (Matthew 4:4).

Trust is also a doorway to being able to understand God's word: 'Teach me knowledge and good judgment, for I believe in your commands' (verse 66). We need to understand the Bible in order to know what it is we're putting our faith in, but is the opposite also true? Must we believe it already, so to speak, in order to make sense of it? We would not expect this in other cases. I can understand a novel without believing that it is a piece of great literature, or that the events recorded actually happened. I can understand a legal document (except for the jargon!) without believing that the laws referred to really exist, or are morally valuable. In the one, I can have a good read. In the other, I can learn something about law.

But in the case of the Bible, we stand on holy ground, and more is expected of us. To understand and appreciate the word of God in a way that benefits us spiritually, we *must* have faith, 'For we also have had the gospel preached to us, just as they did; but the message they heard was of no value to them, because those who heard did not combine it with faith' (Hebrews 4:2).

> *To understand and appreciate the word of God in a way that benefits us spiritually, we* **must** *have faith.*

Where does this faith come from? 'Faith comes from hearing the message' (Romans 10:17). This is a good example of a divine paradox: only God's word arriving in the heart can create faith, and yet the word of God is of no value unless it meets faith already in that heart when it arrives!

So how do we begin? Is lack of faith and lack of understanding a vicious circle from which we cannot climb? No! Although we cannot explain how, we all know from experience that at some point in our lives God miraculously plants a seed of faith in our hearts, and—I believe simultaneously—opens our hearts to his word. For most of us, that moment actually comes before conversion. In my own case, I can remember a two-day period, before I had actually handed over the control of my life to Christ's lordship, when a revolution was occurring in my heart. I was beginning to take Christ's claims seriously. I was beginning to think about the gospel. I was beginning to listen. I was on the path to belief.

Once God has started this process off, he leads us to greater understanding and higher faith: not the vicious circle but the virtuous spiral. It's back to the spiral staircase!

The psalmist's faith in God's word gave him the confidence to pray in line with that word. We see him praying for many things in Psalm 119: for personal revival and preservation (verses 25, 149, 154, 156), strength and sustenance (verses 28, 116), salvation and deliverance (verses 41, 170), comfort and mercy (verses 58, 76) and understanding (verse 169). And on each occasion, he asks God to 'give him these things *according to your word/ promise*'. His confidence that God will answer lies in knowing that he is praying in accordance with God's word of promise. We even see him praying from God's word when the answer seems a long way off (verses 82, 123). This shows that he hangs on to faith even when circumstances paint a different picture.

A heart that hopes

'Do not snatch the word of truth from my mouth, for I have put my hope in your laws' (Psalm 119:43).

It is so important to put our hope in God's word. Christian hope is not the doubtful thing we normally call 'hope'. If I'm standing in the rain waiting for a bus, and the woman next to me in the queue says, 'Oh, I do hope a bus comes soon!', she is almost implying, '. . . but I don't suppose it will.' Hope of this type is a sort of forlorn desire—a desire tinged with doubt. So if I'm

71

asking someone questions to see if he has assurance that he belongs to God and has had his sins forgiven, I will often say something like, 'If you were to die tonight do you *know* that you would go to heaven?' And if he answers, 'Well, I hope so,' then frankly I doubt the reality of his assurance, because I know what he means by 'hope'! Real Christian hope, however, is a sure and certain hope. It is desire mixed with real trust. 'Hope does not disappoint us, because God has poured out his love into hearts by the Holy Spirit, whom he has given us' (Romans 5:5).

The psalmist's heart-cries of faith and hope in God's promises carry a particular ring of poignancy for us when we remember that much if not all the psalm was written under extremely difficult circumstances. 'I am laid low in the dust . . . Take away the disgrace I dread . . . then I will answer the one who taunts me . . . The arrogant mock me without restraint . . . the wicked bind me with ropes . . . the arrogant have smeared me with lies . . . men persecute me without cause.' Despite all this, God's word was effective in bringing real consolation to his soul, 'I remember your ancient laws, O Lord, and I find comfort in them' (Psalm 119:52).

A heart of love

The psalmist expresses his love for God's decrees with outspoken assertions of praise, such as, 'How sweet are your words to my taste, sweeter than honey to my mouth!' (verse 103). These are words of intimate love which you might expect to hear between husband and wife. If we see the Bible as a restrictive and depressing set of rules, or if we find our Bible reading boring, dull, tedious, a 'switch off' time, we will not understand or benefit from it as we are meant to. Some of us have had an upbringing in which the Bible has been presented to us in a way that has left a nasty taste in our mouths. If such an attitude is part of the 'spiritual baggage' that you have carried with you from your pre-Christian life, you need to be set free. Pray that the Lord will give you a real love and desire for his word.

If we see the Bible as a restrictive and depressing set of rules, or if we find our Bible reading boring, dull, tedious, a 'switch off' time, we will not understand or benefit from it as we are meant to.

The psalmist also shows us the intense desire and longing for God's word that this love creates in his heart. 'My soul is consumed with longing for your laws at all times' (verse 20). An easy guide for measuring our appetite for God's word is to compare how long we spend reading the Bible each day with how long we spend looking at the newspaper, or watching the television. Now of course it is somewhat unfair simply to compare lengths of time engaged in each activity, for while we might be spending as long in front of the television as we do poring over the word, we might be giving 'quality time' to Bible reading, and just lounging in front of the screen to relax at our most tired point in the day. Nevertheless, it *is* a guide, even if only a preliminary one. And I suspect that many of us will have to confess that in comparison with the heart of the psalmist, ours border on apathy.

How can we increase our appetite to feed on God's word? First we need to remember that spiritual appetites work the other way round from physical appetites. Go

With Bible reading, we find that the more we take in, the more we want. The more we have, the more we hunger. Increasing our intake actually increases our appetite.

without physical food for a day, and you will be hungry. The longer the gap, the more the hunger. On the other hand, eat a huge meal, and just looking at another vast pile of food can make you feel sick. But with Bible reading, we find that the more we take in, the more we want. The more we have, the more we hunger. Increasing our intake actually increases our appetite. But people who hardly read the Bible have precious little appetite for it and a bit of initial 'force-feeding' may be in order. Read the Bible more than you want to—and soon enough you'll be wanting to read the Bible more than you do.

In practice, 'force-feeding' might mean setting yourself some rather mechanical-sounding targets, at least to begin with. Decide to read the Bible for a certain length of time each day. Or perhaps consider when in the day you will benefit most from reading the Bible. Some people are 'morning people'. Others are 'evening people'. Which are you? Do you read the Bible at that time of day when your brain is sharpest and you are most awake? Or does it get left until you are only at 60% efficiency? *Maximise* Bible reading and *prioritise* Bible reading.

As God gave the psalmist the word, so we find him filled with gratitude. 'Your statutes are my delight; they are my counsellors' (verse 24). 'At midnight I rise to give you thanks for your righteous laws' (verse 62). How can our delight rise to that league? How can our attitude to the

Bible be refreshed? Certainly we can pray for this joy to grow in our hearts. But there is no doubt that it also grows through our putting the word into practice, and seeing that God is faithful—that his word does 'work'. When we *experience* his truth, as well as reading about it, we will be filled with delight.

Some might question at this point whether such a preoccupation with the word might not divert our eyes from God himself. Some people accuse evangelical Christians of 'bibliolatry'—in other words, of worshipping the Bible. 'Get your eyes off the Bible, and back onto God!' is their message. But they create a false distinction. We love what God says precisely because we love the God who says it. Because I love my wife, I love what she says. I want to hear what she says. I care about what she says. This isn't some sort of clandestine relationship with her words! There isn't a dreadful 'love triangle'. Is she *jealous* of my love for her words? Of course not! And the same applies to our love for God's word.

A heart that holds on

'I hold fast to your statutes, O Lord; do not let me be put to shame' (verse 31).

It doesn't matter how much pressure might come to divert the psalmist's attention from God's truth: he will not let go. We need to aim for the same tenacity. What makes us begin to neglect Bible reading, or doubt the truth of what we read? Being tired, or over-busy? Coming under peer pressure, or facing adverse circumstances? We need to identify the things that affect us, and make the all-important decision to put God's word further up our priority scale than those things. We must not allow anything to divert us from it.

A heart grieved to see disobedience

The psalmist's own attitude towards Scripture is not mirrored in all those he sees around him. 'Streams of tears flow from my eyes, for your law is not obeyed' (verse 136). It grieves him bitterly to see God's word being ignored and disobeyed. This too is an aspect of his own love for the word of God. Because the Holy Spirit resides in his spirit, he feels something of God's grief at the way some treat his law.

This psalmist must have had a tremendous grasp of the word of God, but the same can be true for us. God's Spirit within us wants to develop Christ's character in our hearts. Then our understanding will grow, both of God's word and of God himself.

Back to the Bible—for contemplation or discussion

1. From Psalm 119:113–144, list all the heart attitudes to God's word that you see expressed by the psalmist.
2. Can you describe the effect that God's word must have been having on this man?
3. Can you think of examples from your own life where God's word has so touched your heart that your actions have been affected?
4. What heart responses to God's word that you see in Psalm 119 would you most like reflected in your own life?

Prayer

Lord, please help my Bible-reading time not to be a 'switch-off' time! Please increase my delight in your word. Forgive me for my bad attitudes in the past and set me free to have a new and fresh experience of your word.

4
Goodbye to the Mind?

Earlier we saw that to understand and appreciate the Bible we do not need to be particularly intelligent or well-educated. But some people go a lot further than this. They say that intelligence and education are actually disadvantages to understanding God's word, because understanding of the Bible is, in their view, only a spiritual process.

'Stop trying to understand it,' they urge, 'just accept it!' 'Don't try to analyse it, just believe it!'

Have you heard such comments, or perhaps made them? They sound good, and to a limited extent, I agree with them. We cannot contain God or what he says within our limited human minds: he is beyond our understanding. But I don't believe for a minute that we should say, 'Come to Jesus and kiss your brains goodbye!'

I don't believe for a minute that we should say, 'Come to Jesus and kiss your brains goodbye!'

Use your mind

Now it is certainly true that our intelligence must be humbled and renewed, but it must not be abandoned. As we saw earlier, in Mark 12:30, the instruction that we should 'love the Lord your God . . .' includes loving him with our minds. One of God's promises in the New Covenant is, 'I will put my laws in their minds and write them on their hearts' (Hebrews 8:10). As I have made clear already, we must not draw too great a distinction between 'mind' and 'heart' as these words are used in the Bible. But their use together in this verse reminds us that 'heart' doesn't exclude 'mind'. God doesn't somehow bypass our minds when writing his laws on our hearts. It's a process that will necessarily involve our minds.

In 1 Corinthians 14, Paul says, 'If I pray in a tongue, my spirit prays, but my mind is unfruitful.' He wants his spirit *and* his mind to be blessed, so he says, 'I will pray with my spirit, but I will also pray with my mind; I will sing with my spirit, but I will also sing with my mind' (verse 15). What do you think he would have said about Bible reading? Don't you think that he would have written, 'I will read the Bible with my spirit, but I will also read the Bible with my mind'?

The same distinction between spirit and mind is made in 1 Corinthians 2. Verse 11 distinguishes between a man's spirit and his thoughts: 'For who among men knows the thoughts of a man except the man's spirit within him? In the same way no-one knows the thoughts of God except the Spirit of God.' In the next few verses, Paul says that spiritual people make spiritual judgements about things that come from the Holy Spirit (verses 14–15). So we might expect his punch line to be that 'we have the Spirit of Christ'. But no. He writes, 'We have the mind of Christ' (1 Corinthians 2:16). What a striking switch of terms! He wants us to use our sanctified *minds*.

When people say, 'Don't worry about trying to understand the Bible; the Holy Spirit will do that for you!' it's
like saying, 'Don't bother to evangelise; the Holy Spirit
will do that for you!' We know that ultimately the only
person who can convict a human soul of sin and lead that
person to the feet of Christ is the Holy Spirit. He is *the*
great evangelist. But does that let us off the hook of
responsibility in evangelism? Certainly not! We all
know the Great Commission. We have to get out there
and win the lost, *by the Holy Spirit's help.* So too in other
aspects of the Christian life. God wants to work through
our efforts, as Paul makes abundantly clear in Philippians
2:12–13: 'Continue to work out your own salvation with
fear and trembling, for it is God who works in you to will
and to act according to his good purpose.' Thay may look
like a straight contradiction. Surely if God is at work in us
then we don't have to work? Conversely if we have to do
the work ourselves, what place is there in us for God's
work? Actually it is God's work in us that enables our
work for him in and through our
lives. The one would not be possible without the other. If God the
Holy Spirit was not there to help us
read the Bible, all the human
mental effort in the world
wouldn't cause God's message to
get through to us. But if someone
is not prepared to make any effort
at all, God will not override that
person's will and force his word
onto him or her.

> *If God the Holy
> Spirit was not there
> to help us read the
> Bible, all the
> human mental
> effort in the world
> wouldn't cause
> God's message to
> get through to us.*

What sort of minds should we use?

It is not enough for us to realise that we need the involvement and effort of our minds to benefit from the Bible. We also need to know what sort of minds to use. The Bible strongly warns us against using *human* wisdom in our understanding. By 'human wisdom', or 'worldly wisdom', it means 'arrogant cleverness'. Trying to be clever does not open the Bible to our minds, let alone our hearts. Only humble minds can hear God.

In the early chapters of 1 Corinthians, Paul mentions human wisdom several times, showing clearly its barrenness and how it removes the very heart of the gospel: 'For Christ did not send me to baptise, but to preach the gospel—not with words of human wisdom, lest the cross of Christ be emptied of its power' (1 Corinthians 1:17). Cleverness comes up with explanations; humility bows before the mystery and the power of the cross. Also, Paul declares that human wisdom cannot lead to a knowledge of God, 'For since in the wisdom of God the world through its wisdom did not know him, God was pleased through the foolishness of what was preached to save those who believe' (1 Corinthians 1:21). God has chosen to prevent our worldly wisdom from understanding spiritual truth. Mere human reasoning can never form a foundation for real faith.

We need to approach Scripture with humbled, renewed minds. In Romans 12:2, Paul speaks about this kind of mind, 'Do not conform any longer to the pattern of this world, but be transformed by the renewing of your mind. Then you will be able to test and approve what God's will is—his good, pleasing and perfect will.' What does this have to do with Bible reading? God reveals his will primarily through the pages of his word, and it is the *renewed* mind that is in touch with what that will is. In other words, the renewed mind hears God speaking through the Bible.

So how can we trade in our old minds for new ones? How can we switch from worldly human wisdom to the sort of wisdom that comes from heaven? James says that we need to ask for it: 'If any of you lacks wisdom, he should ask God, who gives generously to all without finding fault, and it will be given to him' (James 1:5). He goes on to describe the sort of wisdom that God gives: 'The wisdom that comes from heaven is first of all pure; then peace-loving, considerate, submissive, full of mercy and good fruit, impartial and sincere' (James 3:17). That sounds like good ammunition to use in understanding the Bible!

And how will God answer our prayer and actually inject all that new wisdom into us? God gives us this wisdom as we read. This was what the psalmist found. 'Your commands make me wiser than my enemies, for they are ever with me' (Psalm 119:98). It was also Paul's experience. He wrote to Timothy about 'the holy Scriptures, which are able to make you wise . . . ' (2 Timothy 3:15). We have here another of our 'virtuous spirals': read the Bible and your mind is renewed; have your mind renewed and you are in a better position to read the Bible . . . and so on up the staircase!

Use your memory

For most of us, 'Scripture memorisation' means learning verses or short passages off by heart word-for-word, and for some of us the very thought makes us cringe. It brings back painful memories of having to learn lines for school plays and the like, and perhaps the even more painful memory of forgetting those lines at the crucial moment! But while it may be hard work to commit Scripture to memory, it is well worth the effort. And if you learn a verse, remember to learn the reference too—in other words what book, chapter and verse the words are from. This will help you to find it quickly when you want to show it to someone else.

At my church we once heard a visiting preacher who rattled off so many verses from memory during his sermon that we called him the 'walking concordance'! Compared to someone like him, I used to think I was useless at this sort of memorising. People thought of me as someone who knew his Bible, which in some ways was true. But I had this guilty secret—I was hopeless at Scripture memorisation. What I hadn't realised was that verses were slipping into my memory imperceptibly. My problem was actually one of confidence. Once I decided that I really *must* learn verses, and that God would help me, I was thrilled to discover that I already knew far more than I thought. Now I seem to go through phases of learning; it is not always top of my agenda. But I know I can, and that encourages me.

Having said all that, word-for-word memorisation of verses and texts is only a tiny part of what God requires of us when it comes to memorising his word. In fact, I am not sure that the psalmist, when he wrote, 'I have hidden your word in my heart' (Psalm 119:11), had word-for-word memorisation in mind at all! Another area that is vital is committing to our minds the *overall* message of longer passages and books, and ultimately the Bible itself. Actually, this doesn't demand such hard work. It almost happens automatically. Reading the Bible and listening to sermons will, over a period of time, gradually lead to a knowledge of the contents of the Bible. So just a little hard work in this area will reap tremendous results. And this kind of knowledge is probably more useful than the ability to quote tiny excerpts word-for-word, especially if we don't know the contexts from which those excerpts have been torn! So I encourage you to work hard at getting to know the contents of the Bible. Learn its promises. Learn its commands. Learn its history. Most of all, learn what it teaches us about God.

Why memorise Scripture?

Do a little bit of mental arithmetic. Work out how long each day you spend reading the Bible, on average. Perhaps it's half an hour. Now work out what fraction or percentage of the twenty-four-hour day that is. If you read for half-an-hour a day, that's only around two per cent of the day. Now, if you're not committing Scripture and its message to memory—if you're letting it go in one eye and out the other—God only has two per cent of your time in which to speak to you through his word. And that's not a lot. What about the other ninety-eight per cent of the day? Doesn't God want his word to be having an impact then? You won't always have the opportunity to fish for your pocket Bible. When Jesus

When Jesus was in the wilderness, facing the taunts and temptations of the devil, did he say, 'Wait a minute, I'll have to look it up'?

was in the wilderness, facing the taunts and temptations of the devil, did he say, 'Wait a minute, I'll have to look it up. I'm sure there's something here that will answer that one . . . '? No, of course not. He was able to reply, 'It is written . . . ' The word of truth lived in his heart.

In many parts of the world believers suffer solitary confinement in prison for their faith. Some of them have no access to a Bible. The only Scripture they will have is what they carry with them in their heart and head. They have to rely on what they have memorised. Of course, I hope that such an eventuality never strikes any of us, but it raises an interesting question, which I often ask classes when I teach this material. If that class had all the Bibles removed from their desks, and every door to the room was locked so nobody could escape for a quick peep at the inspired pages, then how much of the Bible could that class remember, as an exercise together? In each class we find ourselves agreeing that with some biblical books, many verses could be recalled accurately, and the overall message remembered. But in the case of less well-known books, we suspect that there would be an embarrassing silence. How much of the Bible do you actually carry around with *you*—on the inside? How much could you recall if you were locked away somewhere and left to yourself? It's a challenging thought.

How much of the Bible do you actually carry around with you— on the inside? How much could you recall if you were locked away somewhere and left to yourself?

86

How to memorise Scripture

There is no doubt that it is easier to commit verses to memory when they are especially speaking to you, rather than as a theoretical exercise. So if a verse in your daily reading leaps off the page, learn that one. Read it repeatedly—out loud. It really does help, even if it does make you feel a bit self-conscious! If you find it difficult, try writing the words out in full. It takes longer to write a sentence down than to read it, and that gives it more chance to sink in. Keep it somewhere you can see it often, and read it out aloud over and over again.

Another thing which helps (as we remember tunes better than words) is to put verses to music. The only trouble is that few of us are skilled musicians who can come up with memorable tunes! Nevertheless, when Scripture has been put to music, for instance in hymns and choruses, then learning verses takes almost no effort at all. In fact I suspect that many of us do not even realise that it is the Bible that we are singing Sunday after Sunday in church. Take the following chorus:

> My heart is full of admiration
> For you my God, my Lord and King;
> Your excellence my inspiration;
> Your words of grace have made my spirit sing.
>
> *All the glory, honour and power*
> *belong to you, belong to you.*
> *Jesus, Saviour, Anointed One,*
> *I worship you; I worship you.*
>
> You love what's right and hate all evil,
> Therefore Your God sets You on high;

And on your head pours oil of gladness,
While fragrance fills your royal palaces.

Your throne, O God, will last for ever;
Justice will be your royal decree;
In majesty ride out victorious,
For righteousness, truth and humility.

(Graham Kendrick © 1991 Make Way Music)

I sang that lots of times before it dawned on me that I was singing a loose rendition of Psalm 45:1–8.

Then, once you have learned a verse, use it! I try to use verses I've memorised next time I'm preaching, and you can do the same. Include it in your conversation. If a natural opportunity doesn't arise, try saying, 'I've just learned such-and-such a verse and I need to practise. Can I try it out on you?' Thoroughly artificial, I know; but so what? The other person might be challenged and encouraged to go off and learn some Scripture too.

Learn to meditate

'Oh, how I love your law! I meditate on it all day long' (Psalm 119:97). 'My eyes stay open through the watches of the night, that I may meditate on your promises' (Psalm 119:148). Meditating on God's word was no light-hearted or occasional thing for this man. He gave it full attention, day and night. He didn't say, 'When I'm feeling sorry for myself and I can't sleep, I get myself off by some heavy pondering on the Bible.' He actually stayed awake in order to meditate on the word.

Meditation is sometimes viewed with suspicion by Christians, because of other religions with their 'mind-emptying' techniques. But Christian meditation is not a process of mind-emptying. On the contrary, it involves filling our minds with God's word. This is how Selwyn Hughes describes it:

> . . . holding a verse or phrase of Scripture in your mind, pondering on it, continually contemplating it, dwelling upon it and viewing it from every angle of the imagination until it begins to affect the deepest parts of your spiritual being ('Introduction', pages x-xi, to the *Every Day Devotional Bible*, published by Hodder and Stoughton).

A good way to think of this process, and one which Selwyn Hughes also mentions, is that it is like an animal chewing the cud. We need to chew over what we read, not just gulp it down. We need to make quality time for this; two or three minutes a day just isn't enough. And let's also use that 'wasted' time: waiting for the bus; doing the washing up; or sitting in the car at the traffic lights.

> *We need to chew over what we read, not just gulp it down.*

When we meditate on truth, we understand more. The psalmist discovered this: 'I have more insight than all my teachers, for I meditate on your statutes' (Psalm 119:99). Presumably the psalmist meant that his insight into every aspect of life was improved as he pondered over God's word. That would certainly include his understanding of Scripture itself. We understand the Bible more if we take time to chew its message over.

Paul knew the value of meditation. He wrote to Timothy, 'Reflect on what I am saying, for the Lord will give you insight into all this' (2 Timothy 2:7). Here we see once more the marrying together of our efforts and God's help. God gives understanding *as* and *if* we make the effort to dwell on what he is saying. Paul didn't write, 'Because the Lord will give you insight into all this, you only need to read it once, and it's there, fixed on the inside of you.' Neither did he write, 'Reflect on what I am saying, because no one's going to help you. You're on your own!' Meditate, and God will help.

Understand the word

Sometimes words are used, in certain forms of poetry and song writing, for example, as an art form rather than as a means of clear factual communication. They are not written to be *understood* so much as to be *enjoyed*. In such cases, the writers may not really bother all that much what people understand by their words. In fact, they may be rather amused by the theories that critics come up with about their supposed meaning. But most writing or speaking has another purpose entirely. We communicate to be understood. And we want others to communicate to us in ways that we can understand, even if they don't sound all that artistic in the process! Have you ever been frustrated, like me, by going into a restaurant that offers food from some exotic part of the world, and finding that the menu is in that country's equally exotic language? You can't under-

We communicate to be understood. And we want others to communicate to us in ways that we can understand.

stand a word of it! It may sound deliciously foreign, but you haven't got a clue what's going to end up on your plate (or possibly banana leaf). Communication, in such cases, has been sacrificed for the sake of art. Fascinating, but frustrating. We want to understand, and we want to be understood. So, is the Bible just art? Or does God care how we read his word, and whether we understand it? Surely a book so full of commands, warnings and promises is designed to be understood clearly, at least to the eye and ear of faith.

And who is in charge of communication? For life not to dissolve into chaos, it has to be the person who is doing the speaking. If every time a surgeon says, 'Scalpel,' the nurse hands him the forceps, will the operation succeed? Will the nurse get promotion? Will the surgeon's blood pressure stay normal? Someone who speaks or writes wants to be understood *as he or she intends*. While the poet may be concerned most about the beauty of the words and their cadences, not caring so much what people understand by his words, that simply won't work for the surgeon. And God is performing a life-saving operation through his word. He gives us clear promises, warnings and commands. And he wants us to understand them.

How to understand

As we saw in Chapter 3, real understanding comes from the Holy Spirit. But how will the Holy Spirit work in our lives to bring his understanding to us?

First, we have already seen that simply reading the Bible will increase our understanding. 'The unfolding of your words gives light; it gives understanding to the simple' (Psalm 119:130). This understanding will be

There may be many passages which seem pretty obscure to you now, but do not give up. Keep reading them, over and over again.

general. We will comprehend God, and ourselves, and our world, better. But within that, it will include understanding of the Bible itself. So persevere. Plough on! There may be many passages which seem pretty obscure to you now, but do not give up. Keep reading them, over and over again. Gradually they will begin to fall into place.

Secondly, remember that obeying the word of God will increase your understanding of it. Obedience comes from an open and willing heart, and it is such an attitude of spirit that will be ready to hear what God is really saying through his word. A hard heart, on the other hand, will almost deliberately misunderstand God's declarations.

A third way in which God increases our understanding of Scripture is to use our experiences of life to broaden and deepen our capacity to understand. This was the psalmist's experience, even through painful life events. 'Before I was afflicted I went astray, but now I obey your word' (Psalm 119:67). He knew that there was within him now an obedience born through pain. How did the new obedience grow? He offers an interesting commentary on this painful experience a few verses later: 'It was good for me to be afflicted so that I might learn your decrees' (Psalm 119:71). The pain actually enabled him to be more open to receiving God's word.

The experiences we go through increase our understanding of the word. They give us insight. Anyone who has had a child will appreciate and understand the biblical passages about being a parent better than someone who has not. Some time ago I was asked by a friend of mine if I knew of anyone who would speak well on the topic 'God's word to the elderly'. I began to think who might be best, and quite naturally my mind went not to my own generation but to elderly speakers. In theory, anyone who knows the Scriptures could put together a reasonable Bible study on that subject. But who would you rather listen to, someone who only knows the theory, or an older person who has grappled with the issues at first hand?

In fact a most suitable speaker occurred to me, a retired missionary in her seventies. I went along to hear her speak, and I know I couldn't have drawn out points for older people from familiar passages in the way she did. For example, she talked about the famous fight Joshua had which he was only winning while Moses, further up the hill, was holding up his hands to God (Exodus 17: 8–16). Poor Moses got so tired that Aaron and Hur had to hold his hands up! She pointed out that these older men didn't join in the fight itself—that was young Joshua's job. But Moses, in his eighties, prayed, while Aaron, his older brother, and Hur, himself a grandfather, sensibly supported him. 'We older ones aren't always in the thick of the battle,' she said, 'but we do have a part to play. We are needed to offer prayer and sensible support.'

Finally, we must *work* to increase our understanding of Scripture. Praying but not working is like asking God for food and

Praying but not working is like asking God for food and then not eating it. Getting the most from the Bible takes real hard work.

93

then not eating it. Getting the most from the Bible takes real hard work. Paul says so. 'Do your best to present yourself to God as one approved, a workman who does not need to be ashamed and who correctly handles the word of truth' (2 Timothy 2:15). Note that word 'workman'. There are no short cuts. Today's society likes to have everything available instantly, from powdered coffee to international communication. But there is no doubt that many of life's most important acquisitions are not instant. They may be gained only through years of investment, and they are all the more precious because of the work that has gone into gaining them.

Back to the Bible—for contemplation or discussion

1. Look at Psalm 119:15, 23, 78, 97, 148. What evidence can you find that the psalmist has made a conscious decision to meditate on God's word, and has not just fallen into the habit by accident?
2. What do you think the psalmist's meditation actually involved?
3. Are you approaching the Bible in the same way? How do you differ? What are you going to do about it?

Prayer

Father, I love your word, and I want to take time to think about all the gracious things you say. Please don't let busyness and hurry, familiarity or habit rob me of the delight to be found in meditation on your word. Please destroy every barrier in my life that stands in the way of understanding the Bible—every one of them.

5
The Bible in Today's World

When I read the Bible, I want to hear what God is saying to me now, *today*. I want it to be right up-to-date and immediately relevant to my needs and concerns. But between me and the original words of the Bible are some pretty large gaps. For one thing, the Bible was not written in my language, English. It was written, for the most part, in Hebrew and Greek—languages which I have not grown up speaking. Secondly, it was written by people and for people who lived a long time ago, in a world that knew nothing of many modern aspects of life such as cars, electricity, and telephones, and who therefore expressed themselves in very different terms from those familiar to the world in which I must live. These gaps present me with some problems.

Of course some parts of the Bible are immediately relevant. When I read, 'You shall not steal' (Exodus 20:15), I don't have any difficulty guessing how I might apply that to my life, here and now. And, praise God, a great deal of the Bible falls into this 'easy' category. That is why, on the day I was born again and the Holy Spirit took up residence in my life, I was able to understand the Bible as I had never done before—immediately and effortlessly.

But not all the Bible is so accessible. If I go just ten verses beyond Exodus 20:15, I read, 'If you make an altar of stones for me, do not build it with dressed stones, for you will defile it if you use a tool on it' (Exodus 20:25). Now I'm at a loss. For a start, I'm not sure that I understand the sense of all the words. What does 'dressed' mean? I know that it's not talking about a stone wearing clothes!

And even if I can understand all the words as they hang together in that sentence, I can't see the impact they are meant to have on my life. I have never built a stone altar, and I am not at all sure that I ever intend to do so—I wouldn't know how! I've never even seen a Hebrew stone altar. I've never worked with tools on stones. The nearest I got was to work on clay and wood as a school child. And I can't see how the action of tools defiles stones.

> *I want to hear God speaking to me now. I want to understand the significance of the words. But because of the gap, I must go on a journey.*

Do you see what I mean? I sense this enormous gap between Exodus 20:25 and my life. I want to hear God speaking to me now. I want to understand the significance of the words. But because of the gap, I must go on a journey. I must travel back to the time these words were spoken by God to Moses, and by Moses to Israel. First, I must gauge what those words and phrases meant to them. In other words, I must understand the original *sense*. Secondly, I need to perceive the impact they had on those people. That is, I need to discover their original *significance*. Once I am armed with that information, I can take the return journey

96

to here and now, gleaning from the original significance vital clues as to what God intends to say in my life today.

Now, you might ask whether all that is really necessary. Surely God can simply override all this stuff about 'original sense' and 'original significance'. Can he not say whatever he likes to me, directly? Well, yes, he can. He can speak to my heart by his Spirit and say whatever he wants. But he doesn't need the Bible to do that. The difference about the Bible is that it is objective. If I say that the Holy Spirit is saying something specific to my heart, nobody can prove or disprove that claim, because it is entirely subjective, inside me. But the Bible is different. It is black and white (unless you've got one with Christ's words in red!), fixed and objective.

So I must seek the *original* meaning. I must try to find out what Jesus, or Moses, or Isaiah, or Paul, or John, actually meant. If what God wants to say to me now through those words in Exodus has simply nothing to do with what Moses meant by those words when he received them from God and passed them on to the Israe-lites, I might as well read any-thing. I could read any book, or even a newspaper, and God could take the words and give them his own entirely new meaning, and so speak to me. I could read, 'Yester-day the Prime Minister spoke to the House of Commons,' and God could tell me in my heart that what that meant for me was, 'Tomorrow I will show you the next step in my

> *I must seek the* **original** *meaning. I must try to find out what Jesus, or Moses, or Isaiah, or Paul, or John, actually meant.*

plan for your life.' You probably think that's silly, but in theory, God could actually do that.

I heard once about a friend of mine who passed an advertisement hoarding featuring a brand of beer. The advert read, 'Take courage.' As my friend read it, God spoke to him about receiving boldness in his heart from God! Hallelujah! God can speak through any channel, and say anything he likes. But what my friend heard God say had nothing to do with what the advertisers intended. What happened on that occasion is probably better defined as prophecy. It is direct heart-to-heart communication. And God does sometimes use the Bible in this way. I might read a passage, and God will use it to spark off in my mind some thought that relates only obliquely to what is written. But I cannot say then that God has led me to the meaning of that passage. He has simply used it as a starting point for inspiring my mind with certain thoughts, just like with the 'Courage' advert.

When God speaks through the Bible's inspired authors, however, he does want *their* meaning to be understood. When you go to church on Sunday, and the preacher gives an inspired message, God wants you to grasp the preacher's meaning. In so far as the preacher is inspired, his thoughts come from God. It is therefore his thoughts that God wants you to hear. How much more true this is of the Bible. God has inspired the authors uniquely, right down to the very choice of their words. So God wants us to grasp *their* meaning, for their meaning is *his* meaning.

Understanding the original sense

So we begin our journey to God's meaning in Scripture by discovering the sense the words and passages had for their original writers. If each of us were handed a Bible written in its original languages, how many of us could read it, let alone understand a single word? How much can you make of the following phrase, for instance: Αναχθέντες δὲ ἀπὸ Τρῳάδος εὐθυδρομήσαμεν εἰς Σαμοθράκην?! Imagine a whole Testament that looked as foreign and inaccessible as that. When it comes to grasping the original sense we owe an enormous amount to the translators of the Bible. May they receive their reward in heaven!

And there's another group of people to whom we owe a great deal: those who taught us to read. Ninety-eight per cent of the techniques that you and I need for understanding God's word were taught to us when we learned how to understand and speak, then how to read, and then how to struggle with comprehension, spelling and grammar. Those school days may have seemed dreadful at the time, but be grateful now!

The original sense of words

Words are the building blocks of meaning. We cannot hope to grasp the meaning of a passage if we do not understand at least most of the individual words. We can get away with not knowing a few, as anyone with a rudimentary knowledge of French has discovered when he or she has tried to read a French newspaper. But the fewer words we grasp the less complete our understanding of a whole passage becomes. A number of things may cause difficulties here.

We may meet a word which we simply do not recognise. For instance, 1 Kings 6:4, in the New International Version, has the word 'clerestory', while 2 Samuel 18:9, in the New King James Version, has the word 'terebinth'. How many of us know what those mean? Of course, the immediate context which surrounds those words does help considerably in interpreting them. So, for instance, the knowledge that the whole of 1 Kings 6:4 reads, 'He made narrow clerestory windows in the temple,' tells us that 'clerestory' refers to some particular type of window. But we still don't know what type.

Now, your assurance of salvation or knowledge of God's plan for your life is unlikely to be rocked by your not knowing the meaning of 'clerestory' or 'terebinth'! But if you find often that you don't understand the words you're reading, perhaps because the translation you are reading is not your first language, then it really helps to have a dictionary available at your side. You will do well not only to read the Bible with pen in hand, but also with dictionary in hand! The *Little Oxford Dictionary* would tell you, for example, that a 'terebinth' is a 'Southern European tree yielding turpentine'. Now you know where turpentine comes from!

If this problem occurs frequently, consider changing the version of the Bible you use as your main reading for a modern one. Languages evolve, with words coming and going, and what was common enough when the translation was first brought out may now be rare enough to have you flummoxed. But even some very up-to-date translations are not all that easy to understand. Generally, the more literal (exact) versions, such as the New American Standard Bible, are more likely to contain obscure words than the 'freer' ones, like the Good News Bible. The Good News translation of 1 Kings 6:4, for example, reads, 'The walls of the Temple had openings in them, narrower on the outside than on the inside.' No technical terms there! In fact, the Good News Bible was translated specifically for those who do not have English as their mother tongue, but have learned it later in life.

However, ordinary dictionaries will let us down when it comes to technical religious words whose meaning we do not know. A word like 'ephod' (Exodus 25:7), for example, will not be in any standard dictionary. There are a lot of words in the Bible that are fairly specific to the Bible and which we will not come across in the street. You try asking someone at the bus stop what 'tabernacle' (Exodus 25:9), or even 'sabbath' (Exodus 20:8) means! So this is a common problem, especially for newer believers among us, who have not yet got used to the Bible's special terms.

Again, using a freer translation of the Bible will help. But even the most informal of translations will not be able to get away from absolutely every piece of technical terminology. The Good News Bible still uses 'sabbath' at Exodus 20:8, and 'ephod' at Exodus 25:7, though it explains what 'ephod' means in a footnote, and it does turn 'tabernacle' into 'tent' at Exodus 25:8–9.

While there is no harm in cross-checking how a free translation handles a certain term, a further answer is to buy and use a Bible dictionary. Unlike an ordinary dictionary, this concentrates purely on words from the Bible. There is a variety of Bible dictionaries available, some

Buy and use a Bible dictionary.

of which are in fact encyclopaedias, the difference being that, when you look up a word in a dictionary, it will define the word for you, but if you look it up in an encyclopaedia, it will describe the object or person the word refers to. And that is what we want. We don't just want a definition of the word 'ephod'. We want a description of this thing. When was it used, and why? What did it look like? What was its significance for the Israelite priesthood and nation?

There are several different Bible dictionaries that are readily available in Britain. InterVarsity Press (IVP) publishes *The New Bible Dictionary* and *The Illustrated Bible Dictionary*. Moody Press in Chicago publish *The New Ungers Bible Dictionary*. All these are of the 'encyclopaedia' variety. A more traditional dictionary of the Bible is the *Expository Dictionary of Bible Words*, by W. E. Vine, published by Marshall, Morgan and Scott. Buying one of these will cost you money, but bear in mind the words of the psalmist, 'The law from your mouth is more precious to me than thousands of pieces of silver and gold' (Psalm 119:72). If we really want an increased understanding of the Bible, then we need to part with hard-earned money for books that explain it to us!

But dictionaries are not the whole answer, because words are like sandbags, not bricks. They are flexible, and the shorter they are, and the more often they are used, the more flexible they are. Look at a striking instance of the word 'world' being used in very different ways, both from the writings of John: 'For God so loved the world . . .' (John 3:16); 'Do not love the world' (1 John 2:15). Are we to have the opposite attitude to the world from the one God has? No! We know almost instinctively that the word 'world' is being used in two quite different ways in these two contexts. We must look carefully at the context.

To add to the problem, speakers and writers sometimes use words without wishing to give those words their 'dictionary definition' at all! They are using the words non-literally, figuratively, and symbolically. And the Bible writers did this too. In order to understand a word's sense as it is being used in a passage, we have to know whether it is being used literally or figuratively, and, if figuratively, what that figurative meaning might be.

Sometimes that's easy. For instance, similes give themselves away by the link-word 'as' or 'like' between the literal thing referred to and the symbolic thing which illustrates it. Here's an example: 'He himself will be saved, but only as one escaping through the flames' (1 Corinthians 3:15). Paul has made clear his illustrative use of the words 'through the flames' by putting in the term 'as'. He is actually talking about *spiritual* salvation, not about jumping from burning buildings. But the picture he brings to our minds is of someone managing to escape from a blazing inferno, only just in time before the building collapses, and unable to bring any of his possessions with him. It is a powerful illustration of someone only just managing to escape hell, and losing a potential reward in the process.

What are far more common than similes in the Bible are metaphors, which have no link word and are therefore harder to spot. Just look at the rest of 1 Corinthians 3, and see how full of metaphors it is: 'infants', 'milk', 'solid food', 'planted', 'seed', 'watered', 'grow', 'field', 'building', 'foundation', 'gold', 'silver', 'costly stones', 'wood', 'hay', 'straw', 'fire', 'temple', 'fool'. Not a bad tally for one chapter! Usually, though, metaphors don't actually throw us any more than similes do. It is the context which shows that the words are not being used literally. To take them literally would simply lead to absurdity. Could you really think, from 'I planted the seed, Apollos watered it' (verse 6), that Pastor Apollos went round the city of Corinth each morning with a watering-can?

If a word is not being used literally, what then is its figurative meaning? Figurative meanings come about when two different ideas are put together in a surprising way. We are familiar with this from Jesus' parables, which are often extended metaphors or similes. With all metaphors, knowledge of the two juxtaposed ideas gives us the figurative meaning. Take as an example the metaphorical phrase, 'A good marriage is an anchor.' There are two ideas, or concepts, there: marriage and anchors. They do not at first sight have much in common. But put them together, and the metaphorical meaning of anchor in this phrase is clear: marriage provides a stable fixed point in our changeable lives. But to know this, we must know something about marriage, and about anchors! So it is with the Bible's metaphors. Take Paul's words in 1 Corinthians 3:16: 'Don't you know that you yourselves are God's temple and that God's Spirit lives in you?' Here we have the concept of the temple put together with 'you yourselves', the readers, the people of God in Corinth. It is clearly a metaphor—Paul's readers were made of flesh and blood, not bricks and mortar! To know something about Paul's idea of temples will require knowledge of the Old Testament's teaching on the Jerusalem temple. It is no good 'importing' to the passage what a Buddhist means by 'temple'. It's irrelevant. We need to know the idea in Paul's mind when he used that word in writing to the Corinthians. And while there were pagan temples in Corinth, we know that Paul's own Jewish background determined his meaning here: for him, the temple was the holy dwelling-place of God's glory.

The original sense of passages

To get a feel for the sense of a whole passage, read it through repeatedly. As you do so, consider the relationship between the words, phrases, sentences, and paragraphs. How does each tie up with its neighbours? How does each part define, describe, limit or condition other parts? What is the main thrust of the passage? What is its climax? What would the author want you to remember above all else? All this takes time. You can't hurry Bible reading.

But we need to watch for the traps! There are occasions when every word in a brief passage is being used with its dictionary definition, and yet the utterance just does not mean what the sum total of those words would naturally suggest. Imagine that you were listening to someone who was using heavy irony—not to deceive but as a way of giving the message real impact. You'd know it by the tone of voice, the look in the eyes, the twist of the lips. Now imagine *hearing* Paul say, 'Already you have all you want! Already you have become rich! You have become kings—

> *Imagine that you were listening to someone who was using heavy irony. You'd know it by the tone of voice, the look in the eyes, the twist of the lips.*

and that without us!' (1 Corinthians 4:8). Can you hear the irony in his voice? He means the *opposite* of what his words suggest. The rest of the verse makes this clear: 'How I wish that you really had become kings so that we might be kings with you!' The New International Version and New King James Version are both helpful in giving this verse exclamation marks. These alert us to the presence of irony. Here's another example: do you think God really meant it when he told the Israelites, 'Go and cry out to the gods you have chosen. Let them save you when you are in trouble!' (Judges 10:14)? They knew what he meant, and they 'got rid of the foreign gods among them and served the Lord' (Judges 10:16).

> *If we miss such devices as irony, and also deliberate exaggeration, then we may miss the sense of passages, however much we understand the individual words.*

If we miss such devices as irony, and also deliberate exaggeration, then we may miss the sense of passages, however much we understand the individual words.

Discovering the original significance

Even when we understand the sense of every word in a passage, and we see how those words hang together and give the passage its overall sense, we often still don't see immediately what the significance of the passage is meant to be. 'Why is this passage in the Bible?' we ask. 'What is this passage meant to change in me?' 'What impact is this fact meant to have on my life?'

Let me give you an example. I have recently read Judges 1:11–15 as part of my daily Bible reading.

From there they advanced against the people living in Debir (formerly called Kiriath Sepher). And Caleb said, 'I will give my daughter Acsah in marriage to the man who attacks and captures Kiriath Sepher.' Othniel son of Kenaz, Caleb's younger brother, took it; so Caleb gave his daughter Acsah to him in marriage.

One day when she came to Othniel, she urged him to ask her father for a field. When she got off her donkey, Caleb asked her, 'What can I do for you?'

She replied, 'Do me a special favour. Since you have given me land in the Negev, give me also springs of water.' Then Caleb gave her the upper and lower springs.

Now I'll be honest with you. My immediate reaction was: So what? What possible spiritual content is there in any of that? What difference to my life can any of that information make? That phrase, 'when she got off her donkey'; why was that there? Why had God inspired the author of Judges to include that apparently inconsequential detail? What did God want to teach me through *that*? I'm not the only one who thinks like that, am I?

Interestingly, when I spoke to my wife about the passage, I discovered that she had preached from it! She had seen what I had failed to see: that Acsah, Caleb's daughter, had his gift for making bold and specific requests. Just as Caleb had asked for Hebron, and had held on to the promise of it for forty-five years (Joshua 14:6–12), so his daughter was ready to make a bold and specific request. My wife guessed, and probably correctly, that Caleb was *pleased* to give her 'the upper and lower springs', pleased to see in his daughter that same determination to have the very best. And the spiritual lesson for us? Be specific in your requests to God. Hold on to his promises. Do not be afraid to ask in very definite terms. Like Caleb, he will be pleased to grant your requests as he sees your targeted faith.

So how did my wife see all this when I didn't? Probably because she took the time and made the effort to study the passage more than I did, and to study it in context. She didn't just look at the rest of Judges chapter one, but she also drew on her knowledge of Joshua chapter fourteen, for instance, and what it told her about Caleb. Perhaps too she drew on her general biblical knowledge about the importance to Israel at that time of land, territory, and inheritance. No doubt, as well, she consciously noticed parallels between what happened on this occasion and what the Bible teaches elsewhere about specific and bold faith.

If we are honest with ourselves (which we really need to be when communicating with God, and that includes reading the Bible), we will agree that the problem of not appreciating the significance of a passage is a very common one, far more common than the problem of not understanding its sense. I suspect that there are acres of biblical material that most of us simply ignore, just because we have no idea what their significance is meant to be.

The reason that we cannot grasp the *present* significance of such passages is that we do not know the *original* significance which they would have had for their human author all those years ago, and for their original intended readers (by this I mean the readers the human author had in mind when he wrote—obviously the Holy Spirit had us in mind as well!). This original significance must be sought, as well as the original sense. If we knew the importance for the author of Judges of the passage about Othniel and Acsah, if we knew the impact those words would have on the first readers of Judges, then we could probably apply such conclusions easily to our here-and-now.

> *If we knew the impact those words would have on the first readers of Judges, then we could probably apply such conclusions easily to our here-and-now.*

Somehow we need to cross the gap which exists between the world of the Bible and our own world. Scripture was written in a different culture and era from our own. A *culture gap* has developed. Some people would find this hard to believe. They feel they are entering a very familiar world when they open the Bible, and they imagine they are surrounded by people who think, speak, and express themselves in very much the same way that they do. They've been so familiarised with biblical culture through years of church-going that they don't see the gaps. But if any of us hears the words of Scripture as if for the first time (the way the people we witness to hear them), the gaps quickly emerge. Take Christ's words, 'No-one pours new wine into old wineskins' (Luke 5:37). What is your reaction? If you approach that statement from our own culture, your answer is bound to be, 'Of course they don't. They put new wine into *bottles*!' Well, don't they? Or perhaps they even put *new* wine into aluminium tanks! But if you know that in the culture of the Bible people kept wine in skins, then you can appreciate the impact of Jesus' allusion to new wine in old wineskins. There are many other places in the Bible

There are many places in the Bible where knowing the background details can illuminate the meaning and significance of the Bible's words.

where knowing the background details can illuminate the meaning and significance of the Bible's words.

Anybody who has travelled from one part of the world to another knows all about culture gaps. The first time I went to the Far East, and worked for a while in a mission hospital in India, I felt very vulnerable and alone. There was a huge gap between the culture that was familiar to me, and that of everyone around me. Distances of time as well as geography create culture gaps, and between most of us and the Bible there lie both. Before I went to India, the missionary organisation was very helpful. Its representatives in Britain did their best to minimise any 'culture shock' by some well-thought-out preparation. They told me about the culture that I was going to. They invited me to a meal that was similar to what is cooked regularly in India. And they got me to eat it on the floor with my fingers—no tables, chairs, or forks allowed! They couldn't exactly acclimatise me to Indian culture. That can only happen by being in India, probably for a considerable time. But at least they helped me to know something of what I would be facing.

We can arm ourselves with information— information which will bring many passages into focus.

A similar principle applies when we turn to the Bible. We can't go back and live in Bible times among Bible people, but we can arm ourselves with information—information which will bring many passages into focus.

In particular, we need some knowledge of the history, politics, religion, society and culture surrounding of the people and events described. We also need to know about the particular background of the biblical books in which those events appear. When were they written, and why? Who wrote them, and who were they sent to first? What was the relationship between the authors and first readers? What spiritual state were God's people in at the time?

How do we gain all this background knowledge? Primarily, it can come from the Bible itself. While information from outside the Bible can be interesting and often illuminating, the Bible itself supplies enough background information to give us sufficient understanding for true faith and godly living. But we do need to get to know the whole Bible. Just as our knowledge of a whole passage sheds light on the meaning of many words used within it, so too familiarity with the whole of Scripture can illuminate individual passages. Again I issue the challenge: have you read the *whole* Bible?

Having stressed the importance of reading the complete Bible for yourself, repeatedly so that its contents become familiar to you, I am now going to admit that there are short-cuts! There are God-given helps, the fruit of someone else's hard labour, particularly cross-reference and chain-reference Bibles, and concordances. Let's go back to an earlier example: 1 Corinthians 3:16, 'Don't you know that you yourselves are God's temple and that God's Spirit lives in you?' I wrote earlier that a knowledge of the Old Testament's teaching on the Jerusalem temple would be necessary to make the most of that metaphor. Now, if I know perfectly every reference to the temple in the Old Testament, then I can piece together all the background information. But what a task! What a demand on my memory! Praise God that in his grace he has let us off that hook. He has given people the idea of producing Bibles which provide cross-references between different passages where the same word is used or the same concept is referred to. There are various different systems, the best-known of which is probably Thompson's chain-reference Bible. Armed with one of these, I can read one biblical passage about temples, and find pointers in the margin to other selected passages on temples. These will help to throw light on the passage I'm reading.

Concordances offer similar help. A concordance is a list, in alphabetical order, of the words found in the Bible, and then a list, under each of these entries, of each place in the Bible where that word is found, this time in biblical order. Miniature concordances, which do not contain so many words, are often found at the back of study Bibles, but their usefulness is limited by their size. Full concordances are usually separate (and pricey!) volumes. Like chain-reference and cross-reference Bibles, they help us to find the various places in the Bible where an idea is referred to. Their advantage over cross-reference systems is that the complete concordances are not limited to somebody else's opinion about what passages you might or might not find it helpful to know about. But their disadvantage is that they only list words. There might be, for instance, a vital passage in the Old Testament about the temple that does not even have the word 'temple' in it! It might refer to the 'house of God'. Look up 'temple' in a concordance, and you will be completely unaware of that vital passage. On the other hand, a good cross-reference system will make the connection of concepts, even if there is no precise coincidence of words.

We can also gain excellent background details from helpful books about the Bible, such as handbooks, encyclopaedias, atlases, and especially commentaries. Commentaries, as their name suggests, offer helpful comments on the Bible's various passages, in a way that is generally designed to aid our understanding of what we are reading. Similar comments can be found at the bottom of each page in study Bibles, but to get the whole Bible, and a commentary on the whole Bible, into just one volume means that the producers have to resort to using very thin paper, or very small print, or a very brief commentary, or a combination of all three! This tends to lead to the comments being so brief that they are of only limited value.

The next rung up on the ladder is the wide choice of one-volume commentaries on the whole Bible. These are a great starting point for Bible study. When I left my home church to go to Bible college, that church kindly gave me the *New Bible Commentary* (published by IVP), which I used for a time as my main commentary for personal reading, and which I grew to appreciate greatly. Now, though, I turn most frequently to more detailed commentaries, of the sort which each take a whole volume to cover one book, or a few books, of the Bible. Popular examples are the *Bible Speaks Today* series (also published by IVP), and the series written by Warren Wiersbe (the *Be . . .* series, published by Scripture Press). More technical commentaries have been written under the *Tyndale* series, once more published by IVP. This has commentaries on every New Testament book and virtually every Old Testament book. These are rather more 'weighty' commentaries, concentrating more on detailed discussion of the text's meaning than on application of the message to our lives. Higher still up the ladder are lengthy and weighty commentaries of a highly technical nature. These are priced beyond the average pocket, and are too technically detailed for most of us.

Where does all the information contained in these commentaries and other books come from? Most of it is simply culled from the Bible itself and brought together in a useful way. So it is information we could actually piece together with the aid of a good cross-reference Bible and a complete concordance. The value of the commentary is thus partly as a huge time saver, but on top of that, it expertly evaluates the relevance of various biblical words, passages and themes to other more puzzling ones.

However, some of the findings stem from other sources, such as archaeology. For example, if we turn to Daniel 5:7, we read that King Belshazzar, last king of Babylon, proffered a reward to anyone who could read and understand the famous and original 'writing on the wall', which was that he would be 'made the third highest ruler in the kingdom'. There's certainly no problem here in understanding the sense of the words, but what is the original significance of being made only third in the land? Why was the king not prepared or able to make someone second highest ruler? Who was already second in command, and what was so special about him or her that the successful interpreter could not be promoted over his head? The Bible does not tell us. But archaeology does. Strangely, when we turn to Babylonia's own records of that time, discovered years ago by archaeologists working in the Middle East, we find no record of a King Belshazzar at all! The last king of Babylon was one King Nabonidus. So is the Bible wrong? Has it made up a fictitious king? Is perhaps Daniel himself fictional as well? Were his prophecies maybe written 'after the event'? No. Belshazzar, Babylonian records tell us, was Nabonidus' son, and reigned effectively as king, technically as prince-regent, when Nabonidus spent the last years of his reign constantly overseas fighting in wars. For all practical purposes, Belshazzar *was* king, and the Bible is perfectly accurate to call him one. But he himself was only second highest ruler in the land, so all he could offer to someone else was to be third highest—again an indication of the Bible's real accuracy. So in this case archaeological findings have made clear a passage, pointing out the original import of a word. Now, it must be said that such information is not vital for faith and godliness. I can well understand the sense of the passage without this background, and there is plenty of significance in it for me without knowing these admittedly interesting facts. I am not saying that we can only understand the Bible if aided by the findings of modern archaeology. I am simply saying that such findings provide interesting and often illuminating insights into biblical passages.

Let's go back to that verse in Exodus 20 about dressed stones and see if even a little relevant background knowledge can help to overcome my difficulty. 'If you make an altar of stones for me, do not build it with dressed stones, for you will defile it if you use a tool on it.' I said how on first reading, I feel a million miles away from a verse like

> **The key to understanding this original significance lies in looking at the passage's immediate and wider contexts.**

that. And while I might stumble slightly over the precise sense of the word 'dressed', the main problem I have is seeing the significance for me now. First I must appreciate its impact on Moses and the ancient Israelites who originally heard those words. The key to understanding this original significance, as I have said, lies in looking at the passage's immediate and wider contexts.

So, what is the immediate context? Exodus 20:22–23, the section preceding the passage in question, is about keeping Israelite worship of God pure:

> Then the Lord said to Moses, 'Tell the Israelites this: "You have seen for yourselves that I have spoken to you from heaven: Do not make any gods to be alongside me; do not make for yourselves gods of silver or gods of gold."'

One commentary paraphrases the thought: 'Since all of you witnessed the Lord's speaking from heaven even though you saw no visible shape, form or representation (verse 22); therefore, totally abandon any thought of ever trying to embody me in a material image (verse 23)' (*The Expositor's Bible Commentary*, Volume 2, page 428). Verse 23 ('Do not make any gods to be alongside me; do not make for yourselves gods of silver or gods of gold') is actually a reminder of what God has already just said to all the people in Exodus 20:4: 'You shall not make for yourself an idol in the form of anything in heaven above or on the earth below.' What follows is new material and is likely to expand upon that command. So we can expect that the regulations about altars given in verses 24 to 26 are somehow going to protect the Israelites from imitating pagan worship, or mixing worship of God with worship of other gods. God's dislike of the Israelites' using dressed stones presumably has something to do with this.

If we now turn to the wider context of the whole Old Testament, we can learn a great deal about pagan worship at the time. We discover that other nations did not just worship the sun and the stars, but also made statues of people and animals as idols for worship (Numbers 33:52 and 1 Samuel 5:1–5). The statues might be cast from gold or other precious metals, or might be carved out of stone. Does using a tool on the stones come close to 'making a graven image'? Is that why God commands them not to do it? *The Expositor's Bible Commentary* suggests this. As soon as somebody got going with hammer and chisel, the temptation would be to 'go too far'—just another chip here, and a good hammer there, and it would begin to look like a man, or a calf, or some other object that the pagans would worship.

The same idea of avoiding imitation of pagan worship probably lies behind Exodus 20:26: 'And do not go up to my altar on steps, lest your nakedness be exposed on it.' This time the reason is more clearly stated, but it is still illuminating to discover that the pagan religions around Israel practised ritual nakedness. And this information we discover from archaeology.

> *Light is thrown onto passages by background information which narrows the gap between the 'them' of the biblical world and the 'us' of today.*

117

To summarise, then, we find that light is thrown onto passages by background information which narrows the gap between the 'them' of the biblical world and the 'us' of today. Armed with that information, we find that we are far more able not only to make *sense* of such passages, but to grasp the *impact* they must have had on the people of their day.

Grasping the present significance

What God said to his people thousands of years ago is actually only of historical interest, however. It is irrelevant unless it leads us into what he is saying now, to us. What we are after is the *present* significance of passages.

We have seen that for many verses, we know the present significance just as soon as we realise their original sense and significance. I took the example of Exodus 20:15, 'You shall not steal.' I don't have to do any mental gymnastics to find out how that verse is meant to make an impact on my life. And there are many, many other verses like that one. The reason they speak so directly is that they are general enough to touch on what we have in common with the people to whom they were originally given. There may be many cultural differences between us and those ancient Israelites at Sinai, but we know what it means to own property individually, so that something can be yours but not mine, and we know the temptation to take what is not ours. There may be slight differences in definition between theft in ancient Israel and theft today, but any such differences are too slight to hold us up as we read this verse.

However, for every verse which speaks immediately and effortlessly to our situation, there are many which leave us cold. The gap between 'them and us' is not so easily bridgeable. The first question to ask is whether the gap can be bridged at all. It might be argued that the original impact made by a promise, warning or command is the only impact that it can ever have, and to try to apply it to another situation is somehow not possible. Might the original significance be the only valid significance? If the answer is yes, then knowing a verse's original significance might be interesting, but there the journey must stop. Discovery of the original impact will not have been a staging post on the journey to finding present significance.

But praise God the answer is that the original force of a saying is *not* the only impact it can legitimately have. Significance is more flexible than sense. For example, imagine reading 'Masters, provide your slaves with what is right and fair, because you know that you also have a Master in heaven' (Colossians 4:1), first as a master and then as a slave. The sense of the words will be the same in either case, but their significance will be different. For the master, they are a restriction (from cruel practices), while for the slave, they are a liberation (from cruel treatment). Now, you might argue that the verse is specifically directed to masters (after all, it says so!), so what slaves make of it is somehow illegitimate, an eavesdropping on talk between free men. But that is to underestimate Paul's inspired common sense. He knew

> *The sense of the words will be the same in either case, but their significance will be different.*

full well that his letter to the Colossians would be read publicly to the whole church (Colossians 1:2; 4:16), and that slaves would naturally hear what he had written to masters. So he would write it all bearing in mind all who would hear it. He wanted his words to masters to be heard by slaves, and he wanted what he said to the masters to have an impact on the slaves.

And even beyond that, he wanted the letter to be read to the church in Laodicea after it had been read in Colossae (Colossians 4:16). He no doubt knew that slight differences existed between the two churches, even if he had not actually visited them (Colossians 2:1). Laodicea was a prosperous and expanding city at the time, while Colossae was in decline, despite the fact that they both traded in the same material: wool (and may therefore have been in fierce competition). And presumably such differences between the cities will have been reflected in the differences between the churches. Their pastoral problems would have been different, for instance. But it was what they had in common that enabled Paul's words to be appropriate and useful to both.

> *It is what we have in common with biblical authors, readers, and characters that bridges the gap between them and us.*

So too with us when we read biblical words originally directed to other people. We have plenty in common with all the people for whom the various parts of the Bible were originally written, even though there are also many differences. Human nature has not changed since the fall, even though our environment has altered so radically. Our sinful tendencies, and need for God's forgiveness, our natural weakness, and need for God's help, have not changed at all. It is what we have in common with biblical authors, readers, and characters that bridges the gap between them and us.

So it is important to remember that Scripture's significance for its original readers is not its only significance. Paul's letter to the Colossians could also have an impact in Laodicea. But can it also have significance here and now? After all, we do not have the slightest shred of evidence that Paul intended his letters to be read by *us*! So surely any significance for us, being entirely unintended by Paul, is merely co-incidental. And if so, is it really all that valuable? Does it have anything to do with real communication, or is it artificially imposed by us the modern readers? Is it not comparable to the significance that a book of British law might have for a Nigerian citizen, simply because some aspects of the law in those lands happen to coincide? The Nigerian may be interested to note the similarities, but they will not help her a tiny bit if she is being sued under Nigerian law!

It is true that significance, as well as sense, is intended by the author. But who, I ask, is the author? In the case of the Bible, God is the ultimate author. Has it come as an enormous shock to him that the Bible, written so long ago, has somehow mysteriously fallen into our hands? Or did he intend it for us? Of course he did! He *designed* it to have significance for us.

Paul recognised this about the Old Testament. It was not just of

Has it come as an enormous shock to him that the Bible, written so long ago, has somehow mysteriously fallen into our hands?

> *Every verse of the Bible should speak to us. If it seems meaningless or irrelevant, that is due to our inadequacy, not God's.*

historical interest to him. He wrote in Romans 15:4, 'For everything that was written in the past was written to teach us.' Every verse of the Old Testament should speak to Paul, as far as he was concerned. In the same way, every verse of the Bible should speak to us. If it seems meaningless or irrelevant, that is due to our inadequacy, not God's. We must not dismiss any passage as irrelevant, but ask for God's help in understanding it.

So now we have seen that a passage's original significance is not just of historical interest to us, but is related in a deliberate way to our lives. We have seen that what relates the original impact to the present one is what we have in common with the world of the Bible. To bridge the culture gap and to discover a passage's original significance, we need to know about the culture of those times, to recognise the differences, and to learn what we can about that different world. But to come forward once more over the bridge and into our world involves recognising *what we have in common* with the world of the Bible. The genuine continuity of our lives with those of Bible characters enables the Bible to have a divinely planned impact on us, thousands of years later and perhaps thousands of miles away.

It is interesting and informative to see how Paul himself applied this principle. Let's look at how he handled Deuteronomy 25:4, 'Do not muzzle an ox while it is treading out the grain.' This of course had a particular meaning for Moses when, under inspiration, he wrote it. It not only had a particular sense, but was designed to have a certain impact on a rural Israelite community which kept oxen and grew grain. Great! But what possible impact could such a rural command have on first-century urban Corinth? Not a lot, you might think. But Paul disagrees. Writing to the church in Corinth, he found a new and relevant application for those same words:

> For it is written in the Law of Moses: 'Do not muzzle an ox while it is treading out the grain.' Is it about oxen that God is concerned? Surely he says this for us, doesn't he? Yes, this was written for us, because when the ploughman ploughs and the thresher threshes, they do so in the hope of sharing in the harvest. If we have sown a spiritual seed among you, is it too much if we reap a material harvest from you? (1 Corinthians 9:9–11)

I don't think Paul wants us to take him entirely literally when he implies that God does not care about farm animals. He, as a well-taught Jew, was aware of every detail of the Ten Commandments. He would have known full well that the commandment governing the Sabbath was designed to give rest not only to humans but also to animals (Exodus 20:10). I think he was exaggerating to make the point that we humans are far more valuable to God than animals are. And if that is the case, it follows that God's principle of providing for hard-working farm animals applies all the more to how God wants hard-working humans, and in this case church leaders like Paul, to be provided for.

What is Paul up to here? Is he playing around with the inspired word to make it mean what he wants? No. He is simply seeing a new significance in the words for a new

What is Paul up to here? Is he playing around with the inspired word to make it mean what he wants? No. He is simply seeing a new significance in the words for a new situation.

situation, while, we can safely assume, happily accepting their original sense for Moses.

And by what principle does he derive this new significance? He goes from the original *sense* (oxen; grain; threshing) to the original *significance*, in which he recognises the principle of provision for workers. He sees a principle general enough to bridge the differences between rural Israel and urban Corinth; one which highlights and applies to what they have in common—workers who need to be fed, and whose very work is creating a resource from which their food can easily come. In one case, the work is physical, while in the other it is spiritual. But that principle remains the same.

We must try to do what Paul did. We must bridge the gap between our modern lives and the ancient world of the Bible.

We must try to do what Paul did. We must bridge the gap between our modern lives and the ancient world of the Bible, whether that be the world of rural Israel or of urban Corinth. We can begin to do so by recognising what those worlds have in common. And it is a lot. Undoubtedly, the differences are obvious. But the similarities are many. God has not changed one bit. And, since the fall, human nature has not changed. So the basic foundations of our relationships with God remain unaltered. We can only live in complete dependence upon him. Our sin remains an affront to him, and requires his full and free forgiveness. By finding these common areas, we identify the bridge over which original significance is carried to have a present impact on our lives.

Take a look at Galatians 5:2 to see what I'm getting at: 'Mark my words! I, Paul, tell you that if you let yourselves be circumcised, Christ will be of no value to you at all.' Strong stuff! Paul could hardly be more emphatic. But, we might ask, so what? Nobody is pressurising us to be circumcised (Hallelujah!). So what do we do with this verse? Do we simply dismiss it as irrelevant? No. We look for the general principle underlying Paul's rather heated point. Then we apply that principle to our own situations. First, make sure you understand the original sense (if you don't know what 'circumcise' means, look it up in a dictionary *now*!). Then study the context some more to make sure you are clear about the original significance. In this case, that will mean not only knowing the book of Galatians, but also at least Acts 15. You will discover that there was a bunch of Jewish believers who strongly believed that for a Gentile to be saved involved that person becoming a Jew, which for men meant getting circumcised. So the significance of Paul's words to the Galatians was a heartfelt warning not to be pressurised into believing that they had to obey religious rules in order to be saved. If we take that general principle over the bridge between Bible times and our situation, and apply it, what do we get? I remember a preacher once speaking at our church and telling us that when he became a member of his church, he was 'welcomed' by being given a rule book several hundred pages long! Was he being pressurised to be 'circumcised', so to speak? Do we maturer Christians pressurise new converts to be 'circumcised'? What religious rules do we apply? Like circumcision they may originally have been God-given, and appropriate. But in our hands have they become pharisaical legalism? Forgive me; I am beginning to preach!

Now let's summarise this chapter. I have encouraged you to increase your understanding of the Bible's message for today by going on a journey:

- *Recognise the cultural differences* that exist between the world of the Bible and that of our own times.
- *Bridge and cross that culture gap* by getting to know the world of the Bible better.
- *Learn some background information* by becoming familiar with the whole Bible.
- *Know how to use commentaries*, handbooks and atlases to supply that vital piece of information which will unlock the original significance of a passage.
- *And then come back over the bridge* by recognising what we have in common with that world, and see the general principles being stated, commanded, promised or warned.

In this way it will be possible to discover what is applicable to you and you will discover what *God wants to say to you today*.

I genuinely hope that you will make the most of reading the Bible. Get out of it everything that God has put there for you, no less (and no more!). Work hard at it, for the more you invest, the more you will gain. To use biblical (rural—let's cross the cultural bridge!) language, the more you sow, the more you will reap. And far more importantly, you will become that much more useful to God, and his name will be glorified in you.

Back to the Bible—for contemplation and discussion

Here are some questions to ask yourself when reading a Bible passage or preparing to lead a Bible study.

1. Are there any significant verses to write down/learn by heart/meditate on?
2. Are there any words I need to look up in a dictionary?
3. Do I understand the overall sense of the passage?
4. What was the significance to its original readers?
5. What is God saying to me today?
6. Am I believing and obeying his words?
7. How might this passage change my life?

Prayer

Thank you, Lord, for your life-giving word. In all my relationships with it, and with you through it, please help me to have a faithful spirit, a submissive heart, and an active mind. So let me constantly grow to be like Jesus.

Appendix

Recommended books

General

How to Study Your Bible by Kay Arthur (Kingsway Publications).

Bibles

The Every Day Devotional Bible (Hodder and Stoughton).
The One Year Bible (Kingsway Publications).
The Daily Bible (Harvest House Publications).

Study notes

Every Day With Jesus (CWR).
Encounter With God (Scripture Union).
Daily Bread (Scripture Union).
Alive to God (Scripture Union).

Dictionaries

The New Bible Dictionary (IVP).
The Illustrated Bible Dictionary (IVP).
The New Ungers Bible Dictionary (Moody Press).
Expository Dictionary of Bible Words by W.E. Vine (Marshall, Morgan and Scott).

Commentaries

New Bible Commentary (IVP).
The Bible Speaks Today series (IVP).
Be . . . series by Warren Wiersbe (Scripture Press).
Tyndale series (IVP).
Expositor's Bible Commentary (Zondervan).

Please return / renew by date shown.
You can renew at: **norlink.norfolk.gov.uk**
or by telephone: **0344 800 8006**
Please have you library card & PIN ready

28 — 9
27 - 3 - S

Madame Verona Comes Down the Hill

Dimitri Verhulst

TRANSLATED FROM THE DUTCH
BY DAVID COLMER

Portobello
BOOKS

Published by Portobello Books Ltd 2009

Portobello Books Ltd
Twelve Addison Avenue
London
W11 4QR

Copyright © Dimitri Verhulst 2009
English translation copyright © David Colmer 2009

First published in Dutch in 2006 as *Mevrouw Verona daalt de heuvel af*
by Uitgeverij Contact, the Netherlands

The right of Dimitri Verhulst to be identified as the author
of this work and David Colmer's right to be identified as its translator
have been asserted by them in accordance with the Copyright,
Designs and Patents Act 1988.

A CIP catalogue record is available from the British Library

2 4 6 8 9 7 5 3 1

ISBN 978 1 84627 156 4

www.portobellobooks.com

Text designed and typeset by Patty Rennie
Printed and bound in Great Britain
by J F Print Ltd., Sparkford, Somerset

For Nathalie, at last

My dog is old. When he is in pain, an imploring look comes into his eyes. I am his God. He doesn't know that behind the God that will save him, the one he beseeches, there is another God he cannot see. Is there another behind ours as well? The dog grovels at my feet. At whose feet must we grovel?

JEAN RAY

I

Somewhere, in one of the many narrative reposi-
tories that have been set up here and there for us
to draw on when the world needs a story, it must be
possible to find the fable that tells us that people, on
their arrival in the realm of the dead, must lay claim
to a trait, one only, that characterizes the life they
have just led. After all, we need to be able to imagine
the afterworld as a pleasant place – that's a precondi-
tion of these fables, and you would have to be quite
naïve to believe that an eternal sojourn in a single
location with everyone who has ever and will ever die

could remain pleasant for very long. According to the fable in question, the wandering souls are grouped according to shared characteristics, from which we can immediately conclude that it must be especially busy in those parts of the hereafter that are filled with people who strove during their lifetime to accumulate as much money as possible, possess fire, become a famous guitarist, famous in any discipline at all, or where the resurrected population consists of all those who let their self-esteem depend on the number of their amorous conquests.

Of course, this fable about the hereafter is actually a fable about life, which is why even notorious atheists can derive a great deal of pleasure from considering it as a hypothetical situation. On that icy day in late February, for instance, Madame Verona thought about what she would shortly confess to eternity's fabled gatekeeper as the chief characteristic of the life that had surrendered its last toehold and was now slipping away from her. It wasn't so much that she was thinking about *what* to tell him – she had no doubts on that score – it was *how to put it* that bothered her.

*

The one characteristic element with which she would summarize her eighty-two years of existence was that dogs had always sought out her company. There must have been something about her, even when she was very young, that made dogs feel safe around her. As a girl she was often snuffled by passing quadrupeds that immediately begged to be patted, offering to shake hands the way ridiculous people had taught them to. Even more intelligent breeds known for their distrust of children caught a whiff of whatever it is that makes dogs wag their tails, and guard dogs that had been trained to foam at the mouth at the sight of a stranger abandoned all xeno-phobia in her presence. In the summer, when many a holidaymaker dumped the family pet on a conveni-ent roadside, she encountered starving dog after starving dog, and would have taken them all home with her if not for the presence there of a mother who could scream entire octaves at the mere thought of a dog. The only thing her mother had ever permitted her was a childish or, more accurately, girlish dedication to guinea pigs, and even then mother dear would have probably suffered a heart attack if one of the creatures had ever escaped its cage. And there was no question of a mother like hers being able to sympathize with the immature grief of a child digging a hole in the back garden to accommodate the shoe or cigar box that would be lowered into it after the last rites that only children administer to dead animals.

Madame Verona had not seen her parental home since the day her mother was lowered into that same merciful earth, after which the house was sold to people who showed no interest in the history of their new dwelling. But if she had just once succumbed to a nostalgic impulse to sniff up the atmosphere of her tender years, she could have strolled through the garden knowing it was rooted in a small animal cemetery. It was highly unlikely that anything would be left of the countless cavy cadavers or the birds that had ended up there after leaving a greasy spot on a windowpane, but with a little effort she could have recalled which animal was sleeping the sleep of sleeps under which shrub. More than that, she could have remembered what all those little creatures had been called: Mimi, Cuddles, Fluffy, Skittles, Bill, Dolly, or whatever names thirteen-year-old girls give their pets and later feel a mistaken sense of embarrassment about.

Nonetheless, in the case of Madame Verona, we should differentiate between a relatively standard love of animals and the power over dogs she enjoyed throughout her life. Although it is questionable whether 'enjoyed' is the right word in this context. After stubbornly bringing yet another pitiful stray home with her (wrong again: she didn't *bring* them, the dogs simply followed her), she endured her mother's predictably hysterical outburst and then delivered the animal in question to the shelter, realizing that imprisonment there was the price of a full stomach and hoping against hope that this dog might be adopted by wiser owners. That last bit is a figure of speech, as it is common knowledge that there is absolutely no point in buying or adopting a dog in the hope of calling yourself its owner; it's always the dog that chooses the owner, even if that means waiting patiently for rain to rust the chain and long days spent marching.

It is hard to say when exactly Madame Verona first became aware of her abnormal appeal for dogs, but she was around twenty when she travelled independently for the first time and ascertained that her peculiarity was just as potent in foreign countries. Of course, many people have been tickled by an unsolicited offer of simple canine friendship and honoured by an animal showing up to present itself as a confidant, even if it's almost always more trouble than it's worth.

She, for instance, suddenly found herself with a sheepdog as *compagnon de route* on a hiking trip through Portugal. The dog asked nothing of her, he simply followed along behind, days on end, through and over the gentle hills around Coimbra. At night, under the stars, he stretched out on the hard ground that bent her tent pegs, and in the morning he simply resumed *her* path, after first stretching his front legs in an ancient yawn that displayed every last one of his rotten yellow stalactites and stalagmites. He made no attempt to demand a share of her meals. And she didn't give him anything either, hoping he would go back to wherever he had come from. Puddles were all he needed and, fortunately, there were plenty of those. Finally, a couple of weeks and many miles later, a stone's throw from Porto airport, knowing she couldn't take him home with her, she rejected him with a pointing finger and feigned anger that didn't come close to convincing him. Then, for the first time, he let her hear his bark, and the sound cut her to the bone. It was a paltry, worn-out yap, no longer capable of impressing even a sheep. Then he turned, in all his loneliness, hoping that a destination would reveal itself.

*

When Madame Verona's thoughts turned to the fable on that cold day in February, another dog was lying at her feet, the kind of farm dog that Renaissance painters cursed for the way the subtle gradations of colour in its coat revealed the copyist's limitations as a Creator, the mass breeding of which must have stopped sometime in the mid-nineteenth century. A magnificent animal with leadership qualities, gentle through and through, but inclined to boredom. She had vacillated before letting him in, considering her age, but the requests people cannot resist are never asked, they are in the eyes, like the melancholy subservient eyes with which he had stared up at her until she said, 'Fine, come in, you can live here, but you'd better realize you're going to survive me, so don't get too attached.'

The hour at which the dog would be obliged to seek a new master was approaching, and his legendary intuition was undoubtedly making him uneasy. But for the time being he didn't let that show and lay on the cooling feet of Madame Verona, who thought, 'This is what I'll say when I get up there – that I've always been popular with dogs.' And it occurred to her that her beloved husband, Monsieur Potter, who had preceded her to the realm of fables, had probably said the very same thing to death's concierge. He too had always had dogs at his heels. And what could be more logical than Madame Verona and Monsieur Potter being reunited in the terrifying emptiness known as The World to Come? Their being accommodated in different sections of the hereafter would make a mockery of beauty.

II

If we took a topographic map and tried to visualize the slopes of the village of Oucwègne, the contours would remind a novice map-reader of a funnel, whereas a seasoned scout would settle for a drain: a gutter in the earth's crust, worn away with immense patience by a river. Because that's what rivers seem to do, they cut the earth into pieces and take billions of years over it. The proximity of a river, a limited knowledge of the Bible and a little poetic licence… that was all the old church builders needed to dedicate the chapel in the valley to John the Baptist. But the power of faith never won out over the muscle power required to climb one of the three hills on the way home after Mass. On peak days, determined by dry weather and less slippery roads, the curé raised his chalice of consecrated Beaujolais to a maximum of six elderly women with well-turned calves, during a tinkling of bells that the congregation was obliged to imagine at the appropriate moments due to a lack of altar boys.

It's difficult to trace the origin of the misconception that people in small agrarian communities are more religious than their urban fellows, but it is possible that decades of the mass reproduction of Jean François Millet's *Angelus* have played a role that should not be underestimated. In Oucwègne, at least, churchgoers were scarcely to be found unless it was when the bells in the tower were pealing or tolling to spread the tidings of a wedding or funeral through the valley. Six practising faithful – it could have been seven if we weren't discounting someone like Jean-Paul, who dipped his hairy fingers in the holy water every week, but only attended Mass to accompany the quavering voices on his violin and thus assure himself of the thing he so desperately lacked as an interpreter of Bach's partitas: an audience. Of course, we cannot exclude the possibility of someone saying a paternoster now and then in bed, especially the insomniacs – given that the sedative effects of a Hail Mary are well known to all those who ever knitted their fingers together under the blankets as a pious child only to discover that the end of a decade of the rosary seldom arrived before dreamland. In any case, Curé Dubois, a former missionary with an incurable homesickness for the tropics, ignored all other suggestions and blamed the secularization in this unlamented corner of the world on the physical effort church attendance here required, not least of all from the elderly.

*

The three hills that made up the village were inaccessible during severe winters and each hill formed its own hamlet as long as there was a crunch in the snow: Biènonsart, Le Pachis and Chènia. It was on the top of that last hill that Madame Verona lived in a house that could have been lifted from a biscuit tin. And it was this hill that she had come down on that cold day in February, together with her friendly stray, legs wide apart to keep her balance and leaning on her stick, the third leg that was by far the strongest of the three. It was already late afternoon by the time she set out, after her catnap and a sandwich to keep her going. The sky had taken on the colour of an old mop and the birds on the branches were in congress about whether to stay or go, familiar harbingers of a long period of snow. And Madame Verona knew that she would never make it back home by herself – least of all 'on her own two legs', if that didn't sound too cynical for someone who depended on a walking stick. After making it down to the valley she looked up and saw from the chimney that the log she had put on the fire that morning was still burning.

If she ever wanted to make it back home, she had

little choice but to wait until someone came by in a car and offered her a lift. Considering the general friendliness of the region, that was something she could definitely count on, but the weather conditions suggested that hardly anyone would be venturing out at this hour. If no one came by – and this was something she had realized while coming down the hill – she would undoubtedly die here in the cold night, because she had no intention of once again resisting the dictatorship of the body. The last time she had climbed the hill on foot it had taken her hours and she had felt humiliated by her own bones. At the top, she had sworn never again to allow herself to be seduced into rebelling against old age, something that could only lead to snooty airs and, on another level, had already driven countless others into the arms of the pharmaceutical industry. They were out there, the people who believed that eternal youth was an ingredient in a particular brand of yogurt and almost made a sacrament of anointing themselves with the most disgusting kinds of grease as an antidote to the ailments of the years, trying to live without leaving a trail in the testimony of their skin. The trees had their rings; Madame Verona did not begrudge her skin its wrinkles, the signature of all her days.

*

'I could die here,' she had said so many years earlier, after seeing the house for the first time with her beloved Monsieur Potter and discussing whether or not to buy it. As if death allowed anyone or anything to impose geographical limitations. They stood together in the living room where they would later put the bed, since it faced east and great lovers like to admire each other by the first, almost tentative, light of day. They had opened the window, looked out over the hilltops, the distant farms and fields where patient cows grazed their dewlaps fatter to please their butchers. They saw the woods clinging fast to darkness, the clouds drifting in formation to their destinations, and the viaduct that stretched across the valley a little further along to make it easier to get from the commotion of one big city to another. Below them the river described its path in calligraphic curls, graceful majuscules whose existence people had almost forgotten since the introduction of the keyboard. And while they looked at that landscape, they wondered whether in the long run they would be able to withstand its simple beauty, or whether they would be swept away by the solitude of these surroundings.

There was their house and there was Oucwègne. Full of villagers they didn't know, who dared to live hermetic lives, if the stories told by city-dwellers could be believed. It would be a leap in the dark. 'I could die here,' she said, and Monsieur Potter lit a cigarette at the window and rested his gaze on a host of ancient trees whose bark provided a winter home for as yet unfamiliar insects. 'Absolutely,' he replied, 'this is a house you could die in and it's a house you could be unhappy in. We'd be mad not to take it.'

As peculiar as his line of reasoning may seem, there is something instructive about it. Someone who is buying a house for life and is happy has to realize that sooner or later unhappiness could rear its head. In the form of disease, old age, whatever. So yes, the question people need to ask when buying a house is, 'Can I be unhappy here too?' And he meant that this landscape could absorb his bouts of melancholy better than any other. They were growing less common, those bouts, perhaps because they were more in keeping with a certain youthfulness he had gradually left behind, but he still preferred to take them into account. A leap in the dark, to tumble into light. 'We'll buy it,' and they filled the empty room with the echoing cries of their lovemaking, smoothed the creases out of their clothes and drove to the notary's office.

A smile appeared on Madame Verona's face as she thought back on it. A curve in thin lips, a single bracket concluding a long, beautiful sentence. A memory of happiness that, in a more wistful key, could also be called happiness.

III

In winter the heart of Oucwègne was located in the former Catholic cinema, a decrepit building with walls still damp from the days when people let out deep, tubercular sighs at the sight of Greta Garbo and Humphrey Bogart – when their deceptive, angelic faces slipped in under the guard of the censorship committee, at least. The silver screen had been carted off after it swelled up from an excess of dark yellow tobacco fumes – which was why the last black-and-white films shown here appeared in sepia – but the suffering of the tormented bricks resumed when

Cécile de la Charlerie started using the place to cook innumerable cauldrons of mussels in aid of this, that or the other. Garlic mussels, mussels in white wine, all kinds of mussels, served with chips and meatballs smothered with a ladleful of tomato sauce; meals that aroused a suspicion of inviolable happiness and demonstrated why the papists had made the Eucharist the core of every gathering. Our stomachs were the first to figure it out: it's not the meeting, it's the eating that brings people closer to God.

But most of all it was Gordon who breathed new life into the canteen of the old cinema by volunteering to man the bar for a few hours each week. It was true that the disappearance of the last café had not shattered social relations completely; everyone had a set of pétanque balls and shared the bottles they brought from home on the village square under the plane tree. While cheerfully getting drunk and watching their balls come to rest further and further from the jack, they got bites on the lines they had thrown here and there into the river, and later they grilled the fish and ate them with their fingers, spitting the bones out on the ground almost irreverently. But that was in the summer, when it was so hot that pear rust broke out and red spider mite in the glasshouses ruined half of the cucumber harvest, the kind of warmth that made it possible for people to spend the night comfortably outdoors when they were too drunk to attempt the climb home. Madame Verona and Monsieur Potter, too, only needed a single party to realize how difficult it was to climb the hill with beery legs. They stumbled uphill as if on the road to Emmaus, but were content at feeling immediately accepted by all of the biggest mouths in the village.

Gloriosas were growing through all of the good memories and the cinquefoil flowered peach. You noticed it in the elation with which they built an imposing tower of dead spruce in March and set fire to it to welcome spring: winter was tough here, lonely above all, and, as long as the embers glowed, those who had come through it drank jenever to make sure they forgot it as soon as possible. That was why Gordon opened the canteen of the cinema during the darkest months. It wasn't a lot. A bar, a fridge. And a basic record player with a maximum volume that people easily drowned out when singing along to the songs of Charles Aznavour, him above all. In the corridor to the pisser there was a plaster Jesus whose plausibility was enhanced by his missing fingers: they made Him someone from here, someone like Tosh, a man fathers used as an example when initiating their sons into the workings of the chainsaw. And, together with a few tables and chairs and a train station clock, we have now covered the building's entire inventory. Wait – we've forgotten the most important thing of all – the table-football table.

The canteen was a clubhouse more than a bar: it didn't keep fixed opening hours and there were no mercantile goals to explain Gordon's flouting of the laws regarding public drunkenness. But if there was one surety in this boozer's shadowy existence, it was the fact that it was a meeting place where the locals gathered every Sunday morning to boast about the number of pheasants shot and strew superlatives about harvests and excess stock.

One of the people who accepted drinks there was Robert, an elderly man who felt naked without his trilby and wore it everywhere except to funerals. After pulling up a chair at his regular table, he always put his box of cigars down in front of him. The cigars were cheap and nasty, inferior tobacco rolled in leaves that gave off more smoke than aroma. The box bore the portrait of a podgy king in nylon stockings, after whom the cigars had also been named, and it was for Robert alone that Rosetta Courthéoux stocked a supply of these unpalatable fumigators in her grocery store; there was no one else in the whole area who would consider taking as much as a puff of this brand, no matter how severe the cigarette shortage. There was something masochistic about Robert putting the cigars down in front of him, as he had marked each cigar band with the exact lighting-up time. The same phenomenon is seen in avid smokers who have started suffering sudden pain in their upper back but prefer to limit consumption instead of quitting entirely, but their motives are undoubtedly different. It was not fear of modern diseases that compelled Robert to time his smoking, but stinginess. He rationed himself solely to avoid exceeding his allotted monthly expenditure. You could say that he had put himself on a diet, even if dieticians generally prefer to keep nicotine outside their area of expertise. And so Robert laid his cigars on the table, eavesdropped on conversations and kept a careful eye on the clock. Everyone in Oucwègne was aware of his miserliness, but people saw it as a disease and never called him to account. They included Robert in the rounds they bought, and when logic pointed him out as the next to buy, no one committed a murder when he missed his turn or suddenly needed to go home.

Robert had reached an age at which it took him a good hour to come down the hill for his pints of beer, and there was no question of his returning home unaided. Once he had made it to the canteen, his problems were solved – he knew that there would be someone there to help him back up the hill. It was willpower and stubbornness and thirst that drove him in the end to descend backwards, leaning on the asphalt with his hands, just like a toddler coming down a staircase, and it must have been a terrible realization that each visit to the canteen could be his last. Because that day was approaching – his upper legs were already swinging like pendulums, shaking and creaking at the knees – and soon he wouldn't make it downhill. Not even like a toddler. It had always been a more or less inevitable event in his future, so he could have prepared himself, but still. Time had finished with him and the Sunday came when Robert was no longer sitting in the canteen. He was the first person whose tragedy made Madame Verona and Monsieur Potter realize that they too could one day become prisoners of the hill, and they were surprised by the laconic way in which the other regulars brushed aside their concern.

The last cigar Robert lit, months after his final

visit to the canteen, was the cigar from 2.10 p.m. His cigar bands had made it easy for Dr Lunette to be fairly exact when specifying the time of death. The hour, at least. For the date, she gave herself a margin of error of plus or minus ten days.

IV

Although his father had hanged himself from a branch at a relatively young age, Monsieur Potter was touchingly ignorant when it came to trees. He couldn't tell a beech from an oak and could just manage to distinguish a spruce and a pine, at least until the Christmas tree industry got involved and started growing all kinds of intermediary varieties, in bizarre colours as well. Of course, as a child, when the arrival of autumn prompted the headmaster to set poetic projects, he had put together the occasional herbarium, drawing up separate sections of exercise book for serrated and lobed, and noting the names of the trees under the corresponding leaves after first drying them for days on end all over the living room under piles of magazines and thick books. The colours of death had surprised and moved him as much as his youth allowed, but his arboreal knowledge never outlasted the herbarium itself. Willows, he could recognize. They were often solitary and polled, lonely but stubborn, standing up to the wind for years. The willow was a tree with the determination of a peasant, a will that could only be broken by a lightning bolt. He recognized weeping willows easiest, but that was because a teacher had once told him that this tree owed its name to the way its branches drooped, as if it were staring at the ground in sorrow while the others tried to claw the moon. The story annoyed him, because he had always thought of weeping willows as cheerful and graceful. Nothing like the pollard willow, his favourite – so different, in fact, that he found it bizarre that trees with such dissimilar characters could belong to the same family.

All this could give the impression that he actually did know something about trees, but he was still never able to tell us what kind of tree his father had hanged himself from. That was probably for the best, because otherwise he might have been unable to resist searching for associations and meanings that were possibly non-existent. For the sake of completeness, we should mention his knowledge of palm trees, which he mainly knew from movies and thought of as deformed pineapples.

Back then, all those years ago, when the notary unfolded the floor plan of their new house and handed them the details of the boundaries, it turned out that they also owned a neighbouring wood. It hadn't been mentioned in any of the advertisements or documents and they had been happy just living on its edge, but the wood was definitely included in the purchase price and now they were obliged to maintain it. Obliged? Privileged!

*

Four worthless and clearly reluctant roads connected the hill to the rest of world and, of these four, Madame Verona had chosen, on that February day, to come down the most difficult. The forest path, whose gradient and impassability were such that on weekends an array of idiots worked their way up it on mountain bikes, guys who were convinced that tormenting the body was the price death demanded for a long and limber life. When they finally reached the top they were pale and immediately began guzzling disgustingly colourful regenerative soft drinks, but the effort had undoubtedly given them the courage to sit through another week at a desk where the pot plants summoned up memories of the nature documentaries that consoled their atavism of an evening. Nostalgia for the smell of sweat had driven others into the arms of a hiking club, and they too parked their cars somewhere down in the village before embarking on the climb in footwear that was designed for long marches in the polar regions. The cameras they lugged up with them betrayed their predilection for the heroic, and not a hair on their heads realized that they were shooting their photos from under rain hoods like caricatures of nineteenth-century explorers. The local hunters wisely ignored the existence of this road full of cobbles that wobbled and were about to let loose completely in the saturated soil. After all, their bodies were empires built up over decades, with bellies like basilicas dedicated to the enticement of ladies who knew how to value a red-blooded man. Even one who alerted any game well in advance by his heavy breathing and the raucous way he hawked up the phlegm that was saturated with the tannins from last night's Pinot Noir.

Calendars had been stripped bare since the last time Madame Verona had set foot on the forest path, a place that more than anywhere else linked her with her husband. Childhoods are seldom happy, but here Monsieur Potter had found it easy to forget his quaggy past while rehabilitating diseased trees as firewood, with an axe at first but, after just a year, more realistically with a chainsaw. He had to slave to do it, because the trees lay on a slope that was so slippery with mulch that he had to anchor himself to the more reliable trunks with a hip belt. Afterwards he had to drag the wood uphill, like a centaur made up of an Ardennes draught horse and a much too thin man, cut it into smaller pieces, split them, and stack them according to precise rules he had picked up from experienced locals. Fire was the primary fruit of these trees and warmth was the harvest. After three years' seasoning, the wood gave them the smell that all gods undoubtedly use as a perfume and heat that makes anything produced by electric devices look like a joke. When the toppled giants were already rotten he left them where they lay, fungi enveloped the roots and worms did what they had been put on earth to do: demolition. In open places he protected the saplings from the ravenous deer, which he compensated with hiding places made of the branches he'd trimmed away. But even when he wasn't working, Monsieur Potter enjoyed being here, seeing the aureoles force their way down through the foliage and listening to the rustling wind, either alone or with Madame Verona, and sliding downhill with her on a sled, the winters telling him that lovers were children, trying to reach back into the past to seize the time they hadn't spent together. Wanting to have shared their entire lives with each other, because love refused to settle for less.

When he found out about his disease, Monsieur Potter resolved to fight one last battle: to stack as much wood as possible, providing his wife with warmth that came from him until she was old. The trees wept resin at his rampant chainsaw. Everything that was diseased, uprooted, blown over or strangled by ivy was split and cut down to size and the garden filled at an industrial tempo with solid walls of firewood. It had seemed like an inexhaustible supply, but that morning in February Madame Verona had laid the last log on the fire. The last piece of firewood that he too had held in his splinter-pierced hands. There had been less and less to hold that he too had held, because if things don't rot, they break, and when she pushed that last log deeper into the fire with the poker, she decided to go down the hill. As a symbol, a meaningless act set opposite a meaningless fact, but more beautiful.

*

Soon it will start to snow again and there will be no sled to leave its furrows in the white. She looked into the wood a last time and saw how, after her lover, it had gone back to arranging things the way it liked them. For years the wars between mosses and barks had been fought openly again, the elms died standing and furious roots churned the earth. Set on revenge, determined to retake the planet, re-establishing its logic-defying chaos, the wood had grown wild. And it was beautiful. *Man*: they should never have let him crawl up out of the water. Perhaps it was a parting kindness from her own mind, letting her think that final thought before dying herself.

V

I don't want you to wait when my time has come.
You can tuck me in, briefly, but that's more than
  enough.
And if, while tucking me in, you smile a sweet smile,
just once I'll forgive you your feigned happiness.

Don't sit by my bed to count the erratic intervals
between my putrid breaths. Don't hold my hand,
which will lie there like a mitten that once contained
my hand that reached for yours.
Don't listen to the grisly pound and rattle

in my chest as cancer does its best
to reconstruct my bones
and don't look into my eyes,
broken in their sockets and adjusting
to the pitch dark of what will be no night.

Leave me behind in that room. Alone.
Because the two of us belong to life.

Please ignore this banality and go,
downstairs, into the garden.
Hang your dresses on the line and I will watch
through the window as they salute me in the wind.
Fry something, onions perhaps, and brown them well
in butter, so I can smell them here, upstairs,
and think, 'My God, she sure knows how to cook!'

But if my legs still hold,
and I hope they will,
I'll grip the banister
that still needs varnishing

and say, 'I'm already upstairs, sweetheart,
I'll see you in a bit.'

VI

As the nearest doctor's practice was in a neighbouring village, virtually the entire population of Oucwègne went to the vet's when ill. It wasn't as if there could be that much difference between a pig and a person anyway, not if the anatomical posters on the walls of Dr Lunette's waiting room could be believed, and anyone who refused to accept the similarities only needed to go down on all fours for a moment. A bag of gizzards with limbs attached, held together by slime and a skeleton. The cycle of scoffing and shitting took place in all bodies, higher and lower, the holes served the same filthy purposes and they all tasted more or less the same to the lice and ticks. There may have been occasional differences in the way the creatures divided their time between fucking and feeding, but they were all playgrounds for bacteria, cocci, bacilli and spirilla, they had the same glands and the same cancers, and anyone who dared to stop and think about it could only wonder why the medical profession had ever split into one order for a beast and another for all remaining beasts in the first place.

Dr Lunette had grown up in the old newsagent's, where the farmers came to stock up on Maas tobacco and hung around for hours afterwards, confident that the beets in their fields would not stop growing in the meantime. In summer, when the door was open and the sheepdogs were snapping irritably at flies, the cigarette mist wafted out, carrying ever louder and more drunken voices with it. The seeds for many of the painful diagnoses Dr Lunette would later make were laid before her eyes in her father's shop. It was largely in that small shop that Gilbert Dock's moustache gradually yellowed from the smouldering stubs he left dangling until the heat on his blistered lip forced him to spit out what was left of the roll-up and immediately use his tongue to slobber another paper shut.

Listening in as a child between the newspapers and the racks of tobacco to all those stories of the ups and, especially, the downs of the various herds and flocks must have inspired Dr Lunette's choice of what to study, and she earned her place in the annals of the village by becoming the first local female with a university degree to stick in a pretty frame. Her ability to rattle off the Latin names of all kinds of phalanges and obscure muscles was taken as definitive proof of her intelligence and, from then on, everyone felt confident to consult her for their own health and well-being. Because when it came to their animals, people around here rarely or never felt the need for medical advice: they rolled up their own sleeves to turn a calf; they needed no assistance to pour disinfectant into a sheep's annually festering arse; and many a man could tell you that a cow with an incurable disease had given him a grateful and somehow loving look when he rested his double-barrel between her two immense eyes. All things considered, Dr Lunette could count herself lucky that she was able to lay her stethoscope now and then on chests that were more than hairy enough for her to maintain her professional pride as a veterinarian, otherwise she would have been forced to go elsewhere to earn a living.

If elderly women were occasionally reluctant to unbutton their pinafores before Dr Lunette's critical eye, this had less to do with the injured vanity a director might ask his actors to express when their character is being palpated by a vet, than with a certain embarrassment due to their still seeing this doctor as the newsagent's little girl, an old acquaintance who was suddenly requesting intimacy with your insides, enquiring about the colour of your stools and asking questions men feared when the years commanded their prostates to falter. The child you had once thrashed for climbing up to your ripest apples could now read the tidings of your body; she was the kind of person who didn't need a first name. The oldest regretted the decline of the custom of wearing hats, because what did today's youngsters have left to take off their heads when they bumped into the doctor on the street?

*

Setting off down the hill to hear his death sentence from her lips, Monsieur Potter had not considered himself any less bestial than anyone else, neither did he doubt Dr Lunette's abilities. But the prospect of ever meeting this woman outside her professional capacity, by bumping into her on the street, for instance, and having to carry out a polite conversation with her was something he had considered anything but desirable. She was a hearty battle-axe, with a hairdo that expressed an aversion to frivolity and heavy glasses that had left a deep, rosy welt on the bridge of her nose. When taking a patient's blood pressure, she tended to grab them in a kind of head-lock, as if anticipating a bite, and when she pulled on her rubber gloves the victim would suddenly shrink, knowing that she had just recently been in a cow up to her shoulder and had been known to describe in detail how much she loved the feel of that moist, visceral warmth.

Every time they had adopted another stray dog, Monsieur Potter and Madame Verona had taken it down the hill to see how much its journey had debili-tated it, discover its age, get it dewormed if it was young and, very occasionally, find out who its previ-ous owners had been. And every time Dr Lunette had adopted a condescending attitude to this couple who took the fate of these ridiculous pariahs to heart. She condemned the sentimentality, the charity, what she saw as the misplaced empathy of human for animal. 'Why are you giving this mongrel a home? You don't know where it's been, it could be dangerous. Some-one chased it off and they must have had a reason.

Have some kids if you feel such a compulsion to be affectionate!' Try explaining to her that she had the terminology wrong, that it wasn't so much a question of their giving a dog a home as a dog having chosen them. Was this the kind of place where a child would dare to let a tear fall on the table where their cat had just had death injected into its veins?

Science had made Dr Lunette laconic and insensitive to the anxieties her tormented patients sweated out on her table. Moreover it was only the strong of character who managed to get in and out of her surgery in less than two hours. Dr Lunette's compulsive yacking was feared more than her rough manner; anyone who had been examined by her knew every illness in the village. She raged about the drunks and the smokers, she raged about those who fried their sausages in large quantities of butter, she called them by name and provided the dimensions of their livers in the hope of their serving as a negative example. No one knew whether veterinarians also took the Hippocratic oath – horses and goats might not mind indiscretion – but it meant that there was no point in even thinking about having a pregnancy terminated in this village without someone else finding out about it that very same day.

The only thing Monsieur Potter had really considered while sitting between the skeletons in her waiting room was his hypochondriac tendency. But the pain that had floated between kidney and lung for weeks on end and whose location he, to Dr Lunette's immense displeasure, was unable to specify to the exact millimetre was, in combination with his nocturnal coughing fits and the threads of blood he found in his saliva every morning, difficult to brush off as a symbol. And since he was, after all, a smoker, she gave her diagnosis without any trace of pity – *only yourself to blame* – and he accepted it immediately. He had no desire to wait for the immaculate white of a hospital room where he would rot away until the ECG plateaued and a beeping machine called the hospital corpse washers to attention and got them sopping their sponges.

We know that he set himself the task of amassing as much firewood as possible for his beloved, warmth he had wanted to give her with his arms. When he had finally finished, he dished up one last serving of love and, God, was he imagining it, Madame Verona swallowed him from below and seemed unwilling to release his penis, even when it had actually grown too limp for her muscles to grip, as if she realized what he had kept secret and wanted to prolong the embrace. That afternoon he withdrew into the wood – *I could die here* – and hanged himself from a tree whose name he could, by then, easily have revealed to us.

VII

If there was one thing wrong with Oucwègne it was the peculiar fact that the previous generation had propagated itself almost exclusively in sons, a plague which, strangely enough, tends to strike remote and sparsely populated regions. There *was* the benevolence of Lucy, the only girl in the afflicted generation, but by herself even Lucy couldn't prevent Oucwègne from gradually emptying. When the morale of those who were left began to flag and the need for relief became overwhelming, Tosh would organize an excursion to a nearby city where the prostitutes were theirs for the choosing. Nights in which they were able to wear themselves out, full of women who would hopefully help them to get a load off their minds as well.

Not everyone looked forward to losing himself in the strumpets of La Neptune because shattering romantic illusions didn't come cheap, and, second, it had happened more than once that they had headed off in the minibus singing like a bunch of schoolboys only to drive back from the girls in a mood of deadly dejection. Later, on the bank of the river, the fool's paradise they were returning from would be good for the requisite tall stories, sprayed cheerfully out of mouths full of sausage or fish, but at the moment itself every one of them had been pushed back into his own cellar. A guy like Alfredo was always so intimidated by the shamelessness of the nymphaeum that he had to drown his fears so thoroughly that when he reached the point at which he could finally relax he was always too pissed to get it up.

*

The reason why hardly any girls had been born here in the last few decades could possibly be explained with complicated diagrams with arrows leading from one DNA structure to another, supplemented by tables of menstrual cycles, but people in Oucwègne had already reconciled themselves to the theory that the depraved seed of drunkards loses the power to produce a thing of beauty. This was a reference to the days in which the north was still destitute and its men descended to these parts to register as seasonal labourers. They let themselves be quartered in barracks and helped harvest the sugar beets. Boys with unblemished faces and trouser pockets worn out from unemployment and boredom.

Many of them had left the area of their birth for the first time, many had never dirtied their hands before. At home mothers and, in some cases, wives waited for their wages and letters. But few among them could write and their pride prevented them from dictating the details of their homesickness to someone who could handle a pen. Plus: they had already drunk their wages, as inexhaustible as they had seemed to youths accustomed to keeping their money in a sock.

And the local girls – eyeing and ogling and giggling and carolling the northerners' looks to each other (photos are all that's left of them now, but in those photos they remain young for ever and bursting out of their clothes) – took the step from virginity to motherhood in one much too fleeting entanglement. Nothing could have been further than fatherhood from most of the fathers' thoughts: as soon as the dung carts returned to the beet fields, the handsome northerners headed home, no doubt after making false promises to ensure that, instead of soothing an angry mob, the stationmaster could watch the snot-wet hankies flap when his whistle set the train in motion. The sons who were born of deceit months later bore their mothers' names, their rotten roots kept secret from church and town hall. Since then a curse has hung over the area's wombs and, apart from a few exceptions, only boys have been dangled over the baptismal font.

*

The dangers of celibacy are familiar from ecclesiastical circles, and the fear of psychological damage gave some of the area's young men the courage to pack their bags and try their charms elsewhere. In the cases of Dominique and Vincent, even with success. Enjoying the privilege of snuggling up against another body had not made them unhappy, not at all, but after a while they realized that chicken never tasted as good as the chicken they remembered. They missed the hooting of the owls, the hills, the tomcats that serviced their harems with noises that failed to clarify whether or not cats enjoyed satisfying their urges, the singing in the canteen of the Catholic cinema, the grilled sausages in the summer under a ceiling of stars... and the homemade wine. They wanted to show their rapidly growing sons how to skip stones in the river of their own childhood, and argued the case with their wives day and night until they wore them down and got them to consent to going to live in that remote hole where lies about your age are unmasked by the hill. And where the climb turned their bottoms into real hams.

*

Damien was less lucky: he remained fatalistically smitten with Lucy – lonely Lucy, a saint in some ways, the queen of the back seat, the rustle in the shrub – and had no choice but to wait until she grew too old to render emergency assistance. Rolling in it, poor Damien. The pruning of his family tree and the resulting inheritances had been more than enough to make him the area's biggest landowner by the age of twenty. Parents looking to farm their daughters out to someone who had it made would have been only too willing to sniff up the smell of the manure that hung in clods from his bones, but an angel had blown the horn of penance at the foot of every bed: daughters were simply not conceived, no matter what tricks and positions people used to this end during their lovemaking. Lucy remained an exception, as if Mother Nature had whipped her up in between times to keep her hand in, before returning to her cruel male-only production line.

*

In the stories they read as children in Sister Zoe's class, boats were rarely boats. They were canoes – no, they were schooners, and they took the protagonists straight to the shores of paradise. But these books never evoked a longing for other places, not in Damien, not in Alfredo, not in Mazza and not in Thibaud; all of the local bachelors seemed immune. They owned the fastest cars and the paintwork was always buffed up like new, but none of them had the slightest intention of setting out on a legendary drive. This was the place where they were almost completely happy; anyone who plays for high stakes knows that most people would rather not tempt fate. They accepted the lack of women. Not gladly, but they accepted it. All things considered, the wound caused by the birth statistics was nowhere near fatal and you never – this was a law! – *looked* for a woman. You found her. So they stayed here, on the banks of the Gemontfoux, where there were verses left to sing and more beer to drink. And see how their chances had taken a turn for the best: Madame Verona had been widowed and she had stayed here all the same.

As if the north had sent an emissary to settle its debts.

VIII

When the abandoned were still lovers, they had sworn that they didn't want to live without each other, they had given each other power of attorney over the meaning of their existence and the disappearance of one would have cried out for the disappearance of the other. With the elderly that is often a natural process: if one drops dead, the other hurries to the grave without any extra effort on their part. But young adults are not yet capable of dying like swans; their hearts are able to bear grief and they are forced to resort to the kind of methods that can be found in such beautiful examples in the works of William Shakespeare. Of course Madame Verona had once told her husband that she would follow him into what she imagined, possibly erroneously, as endless darkness, taking the oath that many lovers had taken before her, and anyone who feels compelled to question their sincerity at such a time has only their own failures to blame.

Was it the smell of meat that set a dog to barking at the marble in the cemetery on the day that Monsieur Potter's last resting place was being fathomed, or had it been drawn there by something else? Madame Verona watched them slide the slab over her sweetheart's grave and walked alone, something she would do on many occasions to come, across the windy hilltop marked with the names of the dead. Names that were linked to the inconsequential history of this village and no longer stirred anyone's lips. Her dead sweetheart had now been entered in the village necrologies under his real name, his northern name, the name that government departments used to write to him and no one here knew.

The villagers had given him the name Potter after hearing that he was an artist and concluding that he must be a potter, perhaps because people here preferred the utility of jugs and vases to the significance of sarabands and sonnets. Not that he was embraced any less gently when it dawned on them that he was a composer, not at all, but the name Potter stuck as an endearment. When Madame Verona finally descended the cemetery path, the dog stopped barking at the marble, followed her, and kept following her. Awaiting it that evening was an enormous meal, as she couldn't get used to cooking for just herself, and a blanket it could mark with its scent. And so, before she knew it, Madame Verona had been drawn into living on for her allotted span.

*

People had expected to see a removals van negotiating the difficult road up the hill, with Madame

Verona returning to a place from her past where she had a thread to pick up, the kind of crossroads everyone passes through several times in their lifetime, where she would now try another turning. After all, everyone had assumed that moving to the remote village of Oucwègne had been Monsieur Potter's idea. It was common knowledge that artists turned their backs on civilization in order to create it; they were hermits, they sliced off their ears or distilled their colours from the Pacific. Poets wrapped their words in clouds, they spoke in mists like nebulists who dipped their brushes in the thickest of fogs, and composers, God yes, composers, they couldn't be all there either.

It was Jean-Paul, by the way – Jean-Paul who bought horses' tails from the farmers to string his bow, and played the sacristan's tunes on his fiddle in church – who drew his friends' attention to the similarity between Monsieur Potter and other, more famous composers. And he named Ravel, the great Maurice Ravel, who had managed to think up a melody that was happy to be whistled by bricklayers, hairdressers, office clerks, managing directors and nursery school teachers, more than once lightening the waiting for incorrigibly late girl- or boyfriends. He too had left the city, in his case Paris, to relocate to a virtually inaccessible hill in Monfort-l'Amaury. The gradient was such that more than once Ravel went tumbling through his garden like a circus acrobat and the movers lugging his things up the hill swore under their breath and cursed his piano as far less than grand. He too had created an illusion of isolation around his staves in the hope of writing his pièce de résistance, an ambition which, as we now know, was realized. All in all, more than enough reason to assume it had not been Madame Verona who had insisted on moving here.

When asked about the nature of his work, Monsieur Potter summed up a few classics – Bach's cello suites, a Barber adagio, Pergolesi's *Stabat Mater* – and explained that a particular kind of algebraic operation applied to these three well-known pieces would come up with what he composed, at least as far as the mood was concerned. Melancholy music that made pot plants grow, and Jean-Paul was not alone in reaching this conclusion. One of the village's rougher characters was Tosh, who purchased a symphonic work now and then and even enjoyed the attention when others playfully ridiculed him because of it. But the one who could tell us the most about Monsieur Potter's work was Charlo, a twenty-stone colossus, a mass of fat and friendliness, insatiable at the table, with hands that reminded art historians of the oeuvre of Permeke. A man who strode between his pigs with a holster on his hip and kept their predestined path to the meat hook short and painless. True in his love for the songs of Daniel Balavoine.

Unless he had absolutely set his mind on it, he was impossible to get drunk, but once in that pleasant zone that precedes drunkenness – a zone which, unfortunately, so many people pass through so quickly – an enormous grin that pushed the flesh of his massive jaws up towards his ears would appear on his face and he would start singing. Or else he whistled the kind of tunes that can be expected from people who have served out a large part of their lives surrounded by birds. Monsieur Potter loved those tunes, and even visited Charlo at home now and then to write them down. But a sober Charlo was incapable of producing anything even slightly noteworthy. That was why people sometimes saw Monsieur Potter leaving his hill with three bottles of whisky and several sheets of lined music paper, headed for Charlo, the most scientific approach since Bartók visited the gypsies with blank scores and writing materials. Once the third bottle had been broached, a whole aviary came bursting out of Charlo, who twittered away while on the other side of the table Monsieur Potter drew lines and black circles at a furious rate, like a stenographer for blackbirds and finches. Several of those tunes were effectively repeated in Monsieur Potter's oeuvre, but Charlo never dared to attend one of the performances, largely because his wardrobe did not and would never include anything that would allow him, so he thought, unproblematic admission to a concert theatre.

*

But it was no longer necessary. The composer was dead, and his widow had stayed on her hill. The latter gave Oucwègne strength. Because if the far-too-premature widows in stories have always been lifted straight from creation's showroom, Madame Verona was no exception. We'll go easy on the paper and ink and limit ourselves to the red hair that hung down to her shoulders in spiralling ringlets; her eggshell complexion; her sunny eyes fixed at eternal noon; her slenderness and suppleness; the smile that set everything free, as pure as mathematics, and capable of inflicting a temporary paralysis on the more sensitive; the unreasonable legs that pedestalled all this; and every curve imaginable to go with it. A body that had been given to someone who no longer existed and was now possessed by a void she loved. A waste of natural resources, whichever way you looked at it. Here she would stay, and her beauty would frump away from the sausages she scoffed with everyone else on the banks of the Gemontfoux. She stayed, knowing that the hill would later become her Calvary and finally her harsh contract with loneliness. You had to hand it to her, for someone from the north. And the day this news passed through these hills – Madame Verona is staying! Madame Verona's staying! – the men sang while pissing globs of froth into the river.

IX

When the ewes could finally lick what they had yeaned with such difficulty, the quarrymen had coughed the slate dust that piled ever higher in their lungs out into the sink, the thermoses had been rinsed, the horseshoes hammered, the fields sown, the hay raked and tedded, the concrete poured, the cords of wood delivered and the money counted – in short, when the work was done and the time had come to forget that tomorrow would be another day of yeaning and coughing and rinsing and hammering and that they would once again have to sow and rake and ted, pour and deliver in order to hopefully end up with something left to count – then, and only then, would the men head for the canteen of the old Catholic cinema for their nightcaps. And because sleep always comes sweeter after a victory, any kind of victory, they split into pairs that battled each other over the table-football table, playing a game that could not possibly be seen as a surrogate version of football, but was a completely different thing, which they judged to be, in both importance and difficulty, far superior to the supposed original.

In utmost concentration they stooped over the playing field, channelling all the strength of their shoulders and arms into their wrists so that, with a bang that was loud but dry, they could send the wooden ball rocketing to the other end, and prefer-ably straight into the goal. They sweated over neat dribbles, feints and crosses, forcing openings in the field and getting so carried away they forgot how ter-ribly unhappy they were without beer and cigarettes. Worse still: anyone who dared interrupt play for a quick slug or a comforting drag on a smouldering fag was in for dirty looks; he had disrupted the rhythm of the game, disturbing their concentration. Curses and cries of joy held each other in check, blunders were made good with looks of intense self-contempt.

It was supremely serious, it was war and, as is well known, war is much too serious a business to be left to soldiers and statesmen. At the same time, a game of table football was a much better opportunity to taste the pleasures men traditionally derive from bloodbaths. The little ball bounced and rattled, clack, tack; the miniature wooden players, painted red and blue, spun on their steel rods; you heard the screws screaming for a drop of oil, and only when a liberating 'olé' had burst from two throats and the scoreboard had been adjusted with sadistic precision was a brief silence allowed to descend over the table for the time it took to wipe a face dry with a handkerchief before the ball was put into play again, backs bent, handles gripped tight, and the sounds of battle resumed. The dreams of the approaching night promised to be the most beautiful when the opposing team had been brushed aside with a bagel; then the winners would hoist the table up off the ground so that the losers could crawl under it in the eyes of all present, as if it were a victory arch. A high-spirited humiliation. Afterwards they dunked their sweaty mugs in the canteen's washing-up tub or distracted attention away from their steaming armpits by using a spray meant for disguising unwholesome toilet smells. The hatchet was always buried on the losers: they paid for the next round and took the liberty of summoning up gout, hernias or other bodily ailments as legitimate excuses for their substandard performance.

*

Monsieur Potter had been able to maintain his honour during these matches, perhaps because he had spent part of his childhood at a boarding school where the priests tried to alleviate their pupils' imprisonment by providing them with an hour's recreation every evening in a room where table football and table tennis made an almost unbearable racket. He had retained some degree of skill and understanding of the game as possibly the only lasting benefit of his years of boarding school – besides his deep loathing of religion – but nowhere near enough to rank him among the better players of Oucwègne. He cherished his victories – he did have them – all the more and the childish pleasure that could be plucked from them had a longer use-by date for him than for the others, who always imagined themselves as good as their last game. The imaginary victory rosettes pinned to their chests wilted the moment their vengeful opponents spat into their hands and confidently slipped a coin into the slot.

Women did not play. That, at least, was the general opinion, and the chroniclers of this village must admit that there were indeed few ladies who armoured themselves in bluff and tried their luck at table football. Whenever Monsieur Potter and

Madame Verona challenged another duo, they noticed how difficult it was to get anyone to play against. The others found it hard to raise the enthusiasm, simply because there was no honour to be had from defeating a woman. Instead of playing *against* a woman, they would rather have played *with* a woman. Because someone who could win with a woman by his side really *was* good. He could have just as easily floored the other team by himself, that was the idea behind it, and that was how people took it. In this game, being a good partner was one thing; being a good opponent was a much bigger thing.

*

Of course the men were delighted to see that, as a widow, Madame Verona still regularly came down the hill to visit the canteen of the old cinema, where one mastered the past by forgetting it, and stories told in her presence cautiously detoured around Monsieur Potter until she was hardened in her pain. As if he had never existed, as if no one could believe that it would do her good to hear people talk about him again. Maybe that was why she was never asked to join a game: people were used to seeing her play alongside Monsieur Potter, their inseparability (unhealthy in the eyes of some) manifesting itself in this too. The assumption was that she would not want any memories of table football beyond those she had accumulated with her husband. What's more, people remembered her taking defeat in her stride, even though the urge to win was the first and most important rule.

The players noticed her cheers and accepted her sharing in the delights and despairs of their games, but never thought of inviting her to join in a duel. Until the day she tossed a coin onto the table, wrapped her hands confidently around the grips on the rods, and said, 'OK, who's brave enough?' They could have taken her gestures as a parody of their own masculinity, and it is quite possible that it was only their self-respect that drove them to other interpretations. Such as: with this gesture Madame

Verona was casting aside her grief, she was ready for a new life. Of course, nobody got a new life, that was just a figure of speech. After all, life wasn't like a story being written in a notebook – you couldn't draw a line under it and carry on with a completely different story in the same notebook. But people liked to resort to that illusion when faithfulness to a memory was making it hard to find the courage to live on. Starting over again, dividing everything up into chapters because you can end them, and constantly telling yourself how easy it is.

That was human nature and that was how humans arranged their history. They drew a line under organized genocide and started a new story with room for laughter, poetry and advertisements for underwear. So that it would seem as if it were humans themselves who were rejecting and reinventing mankind, over and over, as if they had nothing to do with their own past. That was why people found it so easy to make paintings of gruesome battles that had once taken place and find them picturesque.

That was why all genocides will one day become paintings that will be praised for their coloration. And that was why, or so they must have thought for a moment at the table-football table, Madame Verona had begun a new life. Because she could not possibly let herself be loved by another unless the life she had shared with Monsieur Potter had been a different life. Only a new life could let her believe that the old one had died with her lover. This was the only way that young widows could give their bodies without guilt, without feeling adulterous. Because where there's life there's lust.

And yes, suddenly the men wanted to play table football with her. No doubt about that. With her and against her. And her being scared of winning was irrelevant. Because they too were willing to end chapters, even unfinished ones, to start one in which a woman would play a more prominent role.

X

Spurred on by the effects of a bottle of pastis under the plane tree, the bachelors imagined what it would be like to be allowed to make love to Madame Verona. And although their heroic impulses were not completely crushed by the power of their imaginations, they concluded, each for themselves, that they would come back down to the valley after The Great Event as a loser. They could already picture themselves en route, calm yet hesitant, presumably to prolong the beauty that can be found in melancholy, hands in pockets, drowsy, the way you should be after proper lovemaking. But in none of their fantasies was one of them permitted to sleep off his languor in her arms. Because only in sleep are people truly honest. That was when they gave off unsavoury odours, grunted, passed wind and dreamed out loud. Madame Verona would never give that much of herself to anyone again. And so they had to leave the bed, gathering up their clothes and pulling them on, telling her they understood. With wounded pride: 'I understand.' And adding: 'Don't get up, I'll close the door behind me,' before vacillating over a kiss they don't give or give only half-heartedly, symbolically, in the air. 'I'm sorry,' she would say, not to her lover, not even to herself, but to the young man in the photo beside her bed. She would spend the night alone surrounded by the awkward smell of coitus, possibly because one way or the other she had learned in the meantime to appreciate solitude. And because she wanted to cry her heart out. Striding down the hill, the lover would be in no doubt on that score: he was leaving someone behind in tears. Real tears, like the ones shed at the dawn of humanity, when you could harvest salt from girls' cheeks.

Some of them thought that even this fantasy was pushing things and considered the bedroom overly audacious, a place that was tied to her amorous past like no other. Monsieur Potter had undoubtedly left an imprint of his body on the mattress, a hollow she rolled into gently in the evenings, fitting into him, contained in his absolute embrace. There could be no question of her choosing that location when, as a widow, for the first time, she... And they swallowed the words. Not from embarrassment, but to savour them. No, it was cold hard floors you should be thinking. In the most merciful instance, they would try the sofa first, but awkward positions and fumbling and sudden thoughts of towels to considerately avoid leaving any stains would spoil the fun.

*

Of course the man would come first. Too soon, what's more, before he had come close to losing himself in the depths of the rhythm they had found together. But he kept his end up, believing in inexhaustible Negroes who had left their traces in his white man's blood, invoking them, worshipping them, and not for a second thinking that as far as she was concerned he could have suspended his efforts long ago, and the war of attrition he provided as a courtesy came over as nothing more and nothing less than a display of masculine pride.

*

We enter their fantasies, they don't mind, and we see her lying there. On her back. She is naked, completely, because she cannot bear the playfulness of making love with garments left on here and there. That was the old days, sometimes. Here, her nakedness serves to avoid exposing herself more than is necessary, but she alone knows that. She endures it, but her endurance is no submission. Her hands are in his hair, she *has* to put them somewhere. And although that image is open to many interpretations, we feel moved to think that she is doing it to steer him, or rather, restrain him, for instance, when she feels his head descending. Not that. And him understanding: not yet. Because he is building up credit, showing understanding and patience, and his head slides back up.

If we look at those hands in that hair, we notice a finger with a band of paler flesh, the place she wore her ring – *the* ring, because real rings do not tolerate indefinite articles – which she has now removed. Some women shed their rings before committing adultery, no matter how convinced they might be, and Madame Verona was definitely one of them. Symbols depend on the animistic philosophies of their inventors and in that regard wedding rings have it easy. Madame Verona has laid hers on the cupboard, and knows that even a glance in that direction will make her burst into uncontrolled weeping. And she *will* weep. But not now. This evening. Tonight. Lying in her imprint, alone. So she looks up. At the ceiling, we might think, but we would be miscalculating. She's looking right through the ceiling. And if she closes her eyes for a moment, he will think: she likes what I'm doing now, I have to keep this up. He concentrates on a movement, a spot. She thinks: his hands act but don't feel. If she could reach a clinical orgasm, she would have made an effort in that direction, not from desire, but from hunger, a chemical need, but finally she asks him to stop. I'm OK like this; We shouldn't have even started; Let's pretend it never happened.

There shouldn't be a moon in the sky, neither half nor full, and no rain should fall with misleading appropriateness when the lover walks down the hill. There shouldn't be anything, neither day nor night, and he will know that in that instant she is showering. That humiliation, at least, has been spared him. He didn't stay the night, he didn't have to see her creep out of bed, didn't have to listen to the water gurgling in an adjoining room. Because she was scrubbing herself with her sponge to expunge him. Few men can bear a woman who slips into the shower immediately after an embrace, and he was not one of them. Wet and new, she would have lain down beside him with her back unbridgeable inches away and not a trace of their union perceptible on her skin. All overwhelmed by fresh-spring or cool-ocean or however the soap perfume was misleadingly described on the box. The only delight he gave was to one of her dogs, the umpteenth hunting dog, which sat up at the sound of a man coming down the stairs, watched him leave the house solitary in heart and number, and was overjoyed that no one would be staying to compete for a share of her attention.

*

Yes, that was what it would be like, the men knew that almost for a fact, and opening a second bottle of pastis failed to send their thoughts off on another tack. There was no pleasure to be gained from a widow who was doing it for the first time since her bereavement. And they thought it advisable to wait until someone else had taken that thankless task upon himself. They would try their luck later, when Madame Verona had already breached the contract assigning property rights over her body and no longer, or at least less compulsively, thought of Monsieur Potter when a man clove to her mouth. Until that day they would drive their minibus to the young girls of La Neptune, singing and drinking, grasping and grabbing with hands and teeth, and thanking creation for the weakness of the flesh. Unless Lucy let them sing her name and waited in the bushes while they drew straws to decide the order. This was their plan. To be patient – it worked for the trees. Fourteen single men, under the plane tree, under the starry splashes in the black sky, sucking on tobacco-saturated gobs until they were thick enough to spit heroically, deliberating over dreams they tried to hold tight after they had said goodbye and were climbing the hills to their homes.

And no one there to paint them.

XI

Returning to that cold February day, we see that Madame Verona is still down in the valley, sitting on a bench the council has placed there for the benefit of exhausted walkers; the dog lying at her feet in blind trust. She knows that she won't re-ascend, that she has reached the point at which she exists only as past. It is quite possible that her body would allow her to keep going for a few more years – she is counting on strength of will to die today. Snow has started to paint the world white, an exercise in disappearing. Because she will never see any of the things that submit to that covering of white again.

She has never liked looking at things the way you are supposed to look at them for the last time: a town where you have spent a pleasant holiday, now slowly shrinking in a rear-view mirror; a train racing from stripe to spot; the head of a lover leaning out of a window of that train... But now she seems to enjoy it, that kind of looking, perhaps because she herself is already part of that disappearing, who can say? She breathes in the smell of the snow, enough to take a Proust back eighty years, when snow smelled just the same and she dissected that smell for the first time, moulding it into a tiny morsel and curiously popping it into her mouth to let it slowly melt.

But it is her fingers that capture our attention in this scene. She taps the arm of the bench. Drumming her fingers. From impatience, we might decide, and no one could hold our conclusion against us. Or to ease the cold. Even if she's not afraid of the death from exposure the coming night will grant her. After all, she has heard enough stories about reckless mountaineers who started turning blue mid-climb, went delirious and died with a face that was twisted with delight. Looking at those fingers, we notice a peculiar interplay with her feet. As if she's operating the pedal of an invisible sewing machine. There is also a certain structure to the way she's tapping her fingers.

Of course, she's playing the piano, it's obvious. A merry, simple tune she taught to countless children at the music school, because that was what she did for all those years: spending hours on a piano stool with fledgling little people, semi-talented at best, the wildest hope being that they might one day be up to playing a ragged boston or a drunken waltz at a birthday party, more than satisfied with the pre-dictable remark of one of the guests: 'I didn't know you could play the piano! And so well!' Madame Verona had seen more than enough of them, teenage girls who slid their knees in under the piano in a way that showed immediately just how tedious they found her lessons to be.

The boys signed up when they had failed to make the grade in a sport that might have given them some kind of status, girls fell for the dresses they had seen lady pianists wearing on TV – glamour they considered essential to the sound. Or else they were mummy's girls, who dreamed of putting on an impressive, almost perfect Christmas Eve perform-ance of *Silent Night* while flanked at the piano by a grandfather to the left and an aunt to the right, this after the brat had presented her astonishing exam results to the entire family and just before she needed restraining to prevent her from demonstrating her progress as a ballerina. Madame Verona saw the youngsters cooling their dance fury in discotheques where the tarted-up melodies blared out of machines that gradually eroded their musical taste buds, that was her firm conviction, and it would have left her cold if someone had cautiously pointed out that her ideas were buoyed up by conservatism or senescence.

Her students had raged against solfège, invoking rock singers who couldn't tell a *re* from a *si* but had still reaped success and in whose footsteps they hoped to follow. They thought scales were pointless and used the swear words that happened to be in at the time to reject the methods of renowned music teachers. She had seen enough of it as a child progressing year after year to ever-smaller classes; the concept of discipline had been contaminated under the regime of a madman with followers, no one seemed to grasp that an instrument required the very thing that had once been used to hurry the world to an orderly apocalypse. Her efforts yielded, very rarely, an adult who regretted having given up music much too young.

*

Madame Verona knew that her colleagues saw her as *the wife of.* The wife of the composer who was esteemed by some and reviled by others, the way it goes. The longer she taught, the less she felt at home in the world where she had once met her husband. Her: just outgrown childhood, shy, the girl who strode through her days weighed down by her cello. Him: smoking impatiently outside the rehearsal room, the promising young pianist with the dandyish shirt and neglected fingernails. The year before he left to study composition at the conservatoire.

Until that day they were extras in each other's lives, passers-by in a long corridor. Now they were to play together, an exercise, a siciliano by Fauré, and they would never forget it. The result was pathetic, her hands gleamed with perspiration and skidded on the strings, the teacher used the word desecration. But later that same month they consecrated the city's parks, and their arms too were sacred as they held each other while falling in love, and she listened to the encyclopaedic knowledge which young men are so anxious to pass on to their girlfriends. In no time the young couple were referred to in sly asides as 'Jacqueline and Daniel', after a cellist and a pianist who were torn apart so tragically that it was only a matter of time before their lives were filmed. Ah, the days when they were only just budding, all the things that would have at most until this freezing night to come to fruition.

And suddenly she was there at the conservatoire herself, as a teacher. Piano of all things, his instrument. In the staff room during the breaks her colleagues subjected her to small talk about handbags, TV shows, recipes, the advantages and disadvantages of the latest coffee machine, where to go for risotto and which wine one should drink with sashimied fish fillet. Yawn. Conversations Madame Verona avoided with economical nods. On your birthday you brought in chocolates, a staff-room tradition that confronted her every year with the fact that she had forgotten her own birthday yet again, leading others to conclude she was going downhill. *What are you doing up there in that forest? You'll never meet anyone that way. Come back to civilization. Get yourself a bloke. Life goes on...* They meant well, if nothing else.

*

The song she was tapping out on the bench in her last hours was one that Monsieur Potter had written at her request, searching for a melody that would make children enjoy playing the piano. She played it often herself, in her sleep, with her fingers on the sheets. More than once she had caught herself tapping it out on the steering wheel at a red light. It wasn't something she thought about, the tune was in her fingers, in her fingers and in her feet, so that once, daydreaming, she had even driven into the middle of an intersection, forgetting that it was an accelerator she was pressing. She considered this a missed opportunity and by far the most beautiful way she'd had of coming closer to – how can you keep finding soothing names for it? The lowering bowers? – driving to her death while imagining she was playing that tune.

But we would be mistaken to think that, on this February day, Madame Verona was going to let a corresponding opportunity pass her by, daydreaming on a bench, her head a music box that would never close again. It was what she wanted, there was no doubt about that, but she had underestimated the cold and preferred her reunion with the void to be painless. She stood up. Just to stretch her legs for a moment, that was all; her mind was made up. The dog shook the snowflakes from his coat, wagging his tail, glad of a new distraction. 'There's no bone, boy, where you're following me.' But that didn't seem to bother him. 'We should actually find a good home for you first.' She had wanted to go out like a light, calmly and without any fuss. And now she realized that simply dying is bloody hard work and that an awful lot would be asked of her before this snow had melted, the rivers surged like spring and the early lambs were unwittingly bleating eternal life.

XII

Everyone would remember that it happened the year a cow became mayor of Oucwègne. A cow, that's right – more precisely, a Blonde d'Aquitaine, known by farmers as an exceptional beef breed. Her phenomenal rump made her the queen of the annual fairs, her coat of soft-pile carpet had a colour that went well with most furniture, even modern, and when she mooed it was never from discontent but always an apt comment from the sidelines, witty and pertinent. There was hardly a farmer to be found who would prod and hit his Blonde d'Aquitaine to get her into a truck. She was not an animal – come now – but some beauty who, after an adventure with the gods, had assumed the form of a cow. The ancient Greeks had animalized people left, right and centre and their foolishness was still taught today without a trace of irony. And although these sentiments are chiefly attributed to children who refuse to plunge their fork into the rabbit they patted the day before, many a farmer found it simply impossible to bite into his own Blonde d'Aquitaine. A Blonde d'Aquitaine in a field in a valley, that was a happy marriage of body and soil.

*

OK, there was a mayor of course, a real one, with a salary and royal recognition, who showed his face at festivities and bought round after round when elections were due, a man of copious flesh and viscous blood, fattened up on working lunches and bloated from boozing at receptions, obliged to take care of road signs and parking fines, the naming of streets and the enforcement of building zones. His was the signature on hunting permits and fishing licences, the representative of the law, the ostentatious laughter after every joke, the sympathetic nod after every sentence. No one had anything *personal* against the man, but his life took place between piles of papers, his office was a long way away behind the hills, in the city, where he made decisions about seven other communities as well.

What's more, he was a member of a political party, which didn't mean much here because whether the sash was hung over a Catholic, a socialist, a liberal or something else, the sun shone just as long. But here too people had suffered through a war with good guys and bad guys, and afterwards they had thought it more sensible to call a taboo down on political convictions. They had felt the need for a mayor of their own, one who didn't need to divvy his promises out over eight communities, who steered clear of red tape, and whose public burps and farts could never cause offence. Someone without a flag, that was it. Someone they would appoint for just one task: plunging Oucwègne into entertainment for the duration of his term of office. Celebrations, that was what the mayor was there for, to come up with celebrations and games and nothing else. And since those who make their living off the land are acquainted with fortune's daily tombola, they realized that this mayor should not be elected with the means that democracy puts at our disposal, but should be selected by Fate itself: Coincidence. The election was preceded by meetings in which points of view were clarified with flailing arms, and the strength of an argument was determined purely and solely by the volume of its delivery. How to lure Fate all the way to Oucwègne, that was the question.

Finally all present decided that the prospective mayors would need to look for *something* and – after even more palaver – that that *something* might as well be a turnip. They settled on an evening in the beautiful month of July, pitched a tent in the valley and provided so much lubrication that singing would be inevitable later that night. Those who aspired to office were confined in the tent until the turnip had been hidden in fields old Monsieur Canet had made available for that purpose. When the flaps of the tent were pulled back the men hurried out, rash and reckless, sprinting through the streets of Oucwègne to reach the fields, more Elysian than any field had ever been before.

Year after year the men ran through the streets like harried bulls, each obsessed with the idea of finding the turnip. Their haste might have made sense during the first few elections, but several editions later experience had shown that the search could last for days. Not only were Monsieur Canet's pastures extensive, the deep muddy colour of the turnip also made it easy to walk past it without even noticing. It was always half buried, and sometimes the other half was covered with a layer of dung to make sure that pretenders to the throne were kept busy for quite a while parting grass to inspect all the cow pats.

Like much that is infantile, it was highly enjoyable and this system had provided numerous symbolic mayors, each of whom, motivated by pride alone, exerted himself to be the best, the most inventive, the most fun, the most whatever ever. No portraits would ever be painted of these mayors and if the pigeons felt an urge to shit on them, they needed to hurry and aim well, because there weren't going to be any statues to celebrate their glorious policies either. But their immortality was assured, and more genuine too, and after the announcement of each new municipal father the locals danced and boozed until the udders of their cows were about to burst and they all ran off cursing, each to his own milking stool.

*

Everyone would remember that it happened the year a cow became mayor of Oucwègne. The turnip remained hidden for the second night in a row, every turd had been turned over three times already, to no avail. Viking, who was retiring as mayor that year and had had the honour of hiding the vegetable from his aspiring successors, was already being half accused of playing a practical joke – he had the nerve for it – and his repeated assurances that the turnip had been hidden as usual just like every other year were met with despondency. By the morning of the third day it was clear that only Vincent and Damien were able to keep their spirits up for this marathon, and a tense finish seemed in the offing until the turnip was suddenly discovered in the mouth of our Blonde d'Aquitaine.

Statutes were there to be complied with: whosoever found the turnip would be girded with the tricolour sash and had earned the right to call themselves major-domo of Oucwègne for a term of one year. The cow was appointed mayor, there was nothing else for it. The statutes also stipulated that the brand-new mayor would be driven in triumph from the field to the party tent in Benjamin's *deux-chevaux*. Of course, the cow must have thought that her moment had come when they manhandled her into the tiny vehicle. She must have envisaged chopping blocks and blood-smeared butcher's hats. Her future: sliced and wrapped in sheets of red-and-white checked paper. But when she reached the tent and every man jack started kissing her on the mouth, when she heard her owner speaking into a microphone to promise that, given her function, she would not be carted off to the abattoirs, and when she was finally presented with a trough of beer, she grew calmer. Also specified by the statutes: that the incoming and outgoing mayors dance together. Which they did. Viking wasn't much of a one for ballroom dancing, never had been, but the number he performed with the cow demonstrated clear progress in that area. The end of this party is veiled from memory, but there can be no doubt that everyone there, united in friendship, wrapped arms around each other and forgot the death knell.

Blonde d'Aquitaine, the village's first female de facto mayor, grazed her field from that day on with a sash around her bulk. Anyone passing the field greeted her with a friendly 'Good morning, Madame Mairesse,' and on holy days they treated her to garlic bread. But she didn't organize any festivities.

*

Anyway, everyone would remember that it happened when she was made mayor and Charlo was the first to break the news: Madame Verona had been seen with a man. And not just that, Madame Verona had been seen with a man *in her wood*. Furthermore, the man in that wood had worn a suit, Sundayfied from head to toe, the kind of get-up that would have any local immediately rolling with laughter. Whether or not she was holding his hand could not be verified. But soon after, she gave Charlo the job of cutting down the tree her husband had hanged himself from – to the immense joy of the wifeless. Because this was a turning point; a clearer statement could not be imagined. Madame Verona had permanently cast aside her mourning. And if she started something with the besuited gibbon it would simply be a matter of time, waiting until the plates started flying through the living room and then risking a shot yourself. Who would have thought of her deciding to get that highly significant tree chopped down in such a bloody rush?

Cows were harbingers of beauty, it's true. But until that moment their holiness had been known only in India.

XIII

When Rosetta Courthéoux pulled down the shutters in front of her shop for the last time, everyone knew the years of loneliness and isolation had come to stay. She had lowered them slowly, like a flag after the 'Last Post', but anyone attempting to attribute symbolic worth to that slowness was forgetting her age: deteriorating was the only thing she could do at any kind of pace any more, and beyond that Rosetta Courthéoux had completely lost her sense of rhythm. She had been hearing it from all sides for quite a while now ('For goodness' sake,

Rosetta, what are you doing spending all your time in that shop of yours, wouldn't it be better to enjoy the years you have left?'), but no one's queuing up to support a shopkeeper in retirement, and as long as she manned her counter she was assured of her daily chit-chat. She had sold virtually everything there was to sell at some stage of her life and whenever someone requested something she didn't have, she got it in straight away, often in too large a quantity. Everyone remembered how the jars of salted herring had stood there on the shelf unsold for eighteen years. Children came in just to gawp at them, staring goggle-eyed at the processes of biological decay. Hard-to-sell vegetables were left to ferment in their tins for years, sometimes resulting in a rupture that left the stench of, summa summarum, five hundred gallons of liquid manure lingering in the shop for weeks.

But in her eyes nothing was unsellable, a principle that modern sales managers have cribbed from grocers, and she ensured her place in the stories that people never got tired of telling by actually selling her eighteen-year-old herrings – to a Swede with a traditional attachment to feasting on rotten fish. She took it as a matter of pride that not one product she had ever ordered should be removed from her stock. Even when it became obvious that Oucwègne was doomed to die out and the last child to be born in the immediate vicinity had started growing hair in unpleasant places, she still refused to remove the boxes of nappies from her inventory. And lo and behold, that day too arrived when people stood in her shop waiting until the other customers had exchanged their last bits of gossip and left them alone to ask, 'Rosetta, those nappies you used to sell here all those years ago, have you got any of them left in your shed?' The sizes were too small, no doubt about that, but if you pulled a pair of underpants on over the top, those nappies were still good for hiding the first leaks of old age.

*

Rosetta had more faith in her head than in calcula-
tors, which she considered too slow and mistrusted
as a source of intellectual sluggishness. It took her no
time at all to spit out how much the customer had to
hand over and if her total was met by incredulous
looks from someone who, in department stores,
had lost their faith in algebra, she would draw up
lightning-fast columns in the margins of old newspapers and do the sums over again out loud as proof.
She was no fonder of bank cards, because what good
was money you couldn't hold in your hand? If you
wanted visible goods, you had to pay with visible
money – for her it was that simple.

But since the world had evolved in a direction
that required the memorization of a combination of
numbers before people could extract their own
money from a hole in a wall, and because the nearest
money-distributing machine was a good twelve miles
away (a trip the elderly undertook less and less frequently, and when they did it was often in vain as the
machines were just as likely to be empty), Rosetta

Courthéoux didn't argue about postponing payment. She noted the name of the debtor and the credit extended in exercise books she kept for that purpose. Given her elephantine memory this would have been unnecessary, except for the fact that for the last twenty years of his life Corneille got off with the excuse that the cash machines had run out of money, the bus to town hadn't shown up, his pass had been swallowed... but that he would pay tomorrow, no matter what, and he swore it on his mother's soul and his dog's head. It was never more than bread, a packet of tobacco and a can of beer, and although she knew very well that Corneille would never ever pay his bills, she kept selling him everything on credit. Corneille was a hopeless case, her almost daily excuse for a good deed.

It was an unstoried Tuesday when Corneille stood fidgeting in her shop, letting everyone else jump the queue with the words, 'Go on, I'm in no hurry,' so that Rosetta thought, 'The poor devil, he's reached that stage too, in a minute he'll ask for a box of nappies, promising to come and pay as soon as he can.' But when he was finally left as the last person in the shop, he reached into his back pocket for his wallet, a leather notecase that had moulded itself to the shape of his buttock and almost fell apart like an old Bible, and said, 'Rosetta, you can cross me off in those books of yours, I made it to the bank.'

What surprised her most was that, when going through her exercise books to work out the debt that had accrued over twenty years, she established that Corneille must have had exercise books of his own at home. The amount he laid on her table just before closing time was correct to the last centime. Had Corneille changed his sheets for the first time in all those years and rediscovered his savings? Had an inheritance fallen into his hands, or had he invested the little he had in the national lottery? Or was he one of the many rich people who lead a poverty-stricken life because they're terrified of one day having to buy too many drinks at the pub? These were questions she would never ask him; she was much too polite. But now that the money was lying on her table she realized that Corneille had been her private pension fund. She could close the shop and dawdle along to her last days.

*

It was irreversible, no one suffered any illusions on that score – Oucwègne would speedily join the names of all those other villages that had been sacrificed on the altar of mobility: Bergimont, Charnet, Chersin, Sedrones, Franfays…

Someone had once settled here, a hunter, a fisherman, and when others joined him, they needed to think up a name for the hamlet, because no one ever comes from nowhere, a place that can't be named isn't part of any stories. Someone must have suggested the name Oucwègne and, after tasting the sound of it, the community accepted that name and embraced it. The name would have a future, it would arouse expectations when it appeared on an envelope in a girl's handwriting. Birds didn't need names – every year they returned to their summer residences from the south, and they would keep doing that. But mankind had abandoned this place, drawn to where people become population and the only scenery is cityscape.

Those who stayed, just forty of them, well… they stayed. Unless they had children, because they had seen that tragedy acted out for them by Vincent, intertwined with this village on every side, Monsieur le Président, but one day his children decided he was too old to stay on alone. A giant of a man, big and round, Vincent had a horn in his swollen throat he used to drown out the bullfrogs when the croaking got on his nerves. A man who believed that a diet of five steaks a day would make him immortal, even if he was constantly sucking on the fags he rolled with strong shag. It was, however, his kidneys that gave him trouble and turned him into a stone pisser. 'You don't drink enough!' Dr Lunette told him, adding, 'Water!' to retain some semblance of credibility. He didn't consume *any* water. Water was for cows, which reminded him that Dr Lunette was still an animal doctor. And he would not drink water, not if his life depended on it – he too had his pride. But his children insisted that he move to the city, to one of those homes where white aprons take care of the elderly. Comfort would await him, but he could forget about asking for a second piece of meat. Here he had always been the strongest, the Hercules everyone was only too keen to turn to for help, and it was heartbreaking to see this man – still impressive to look at, but now weak – being put in the car by his children. He cursed them, threatening to die tomorrow to rack their consciences. He drove down the hill spitting, looking at the pale blue winter sky he had always loved and would never see again unless it was through much too clean windows.

And those who stayed, thirty-nine of them now, well… they stayed. With their pétanque balls and their bottles of pastis under the plane tree, and their Aznavour songs that had begun sounding more and more like one potato, two potato, three potato, four.

XIV

'*You'll have to forgive me for being so blunt, but your husband would have made my life a lot easier if he'd hanged himself from a spruce.*'

*

Yes, that wood. It was the end of the nesting season, the period in which foresters forgot their axes and kept away from their domains. That was the only way the squirrels and birds of prey could work on their dreys and eyries, the only way life could return to the foliage and undergrowth. The trees needed the animals as much as the animals needed the trees. In early July people pulled the laces of their boots tight for the first time since March and stepped timorously into the woods, looking for damage caused by the storms of late spring, beeches that had been blasted by lightning and places where deer had feasted on juicy young shoots. Those who sold their timber on the stump removed sections of bark or used paint and brush to indicate which trunks were on offer.

A lot had changed around here and if you so much as touched upon the subject the local operators would take a cut of tobacco between their fingers and dish up the whole story with sublime swearing. About how timber used to pay. When people still scraped the bowels of the earth to mine coal. They couldn't keep up with the demand, because the companies burrowed deeper and deeper under the ground and the mineshafts needed stronger and stronger shoring with good timber you couldn't plant enough of. Real money, mister, hand over foot, in those days a forest was an earner. But the mines closed down, suddenly, becoming the silent graves of acres and acres of sacrificed woods and Italians who were never found again: young guys, determined to one day return to Lettomanoppello or God knows what they called their particular brand of homesickness, where they would take the most beautiful girl in their arms under the campanile. Buried alive one catastrophic morning. Ah, even those who mourned them have long since passed away.

Coffins, that's what the trees became in the days that followed, coffins for the ones they managed to bring up in bits and pieces. The cheapest kind, from the plainest planks, because the disaster only struck the humble, as the newspapers of the time wrote. But after that, end of story. The pits closed, the pitmen disappeared, and with them the demand for wood. Switching to other kinds of wood, for furniture-making, for instance, wasn't the kind of thing you did overnight. A tree doesn't even catch your eye until it's thirty years old, but if you want to cut a table out of it, you've still got a long wait in front of you.

On top of that, the declaration proper of the war on trees was yet to come, as contradictory as this may sound, when plastic and aluminium suddenly filled the houses. The demand for wood plummeted, the economic value of one of these woods was more or less zilch, and most owners had no choice but to turn to something else to make a living. Not forgetting that meanwhile they had penetrated deep into the Amazonian forests, shamelessly clearing trees that had reached up to the heavens for centuries without human intervention at a rate of dozens of football pitches per hour. Per minute. And paper – that, they recycled. Only fucking morons were left in forestry, that and the odd solipsist here and there, people who had money left under a mattress to invest in the solitude they needed after dissecting mankind so thoroughly that misanthropy was the only possible outcome. Other than that: no one.

Although. Firewood, there were still people in firewood here and there. Firewood and Christmas.

*

Madame Verona accompanied the besuited gentle-
man into the wood thinking of cathedrals. The
comparison was Monsieur Potter's who, when guiding the competition between the dominant trees,
realized that he would never see the fruits of his
labour. Healthy forests need proud old trees – in
a way they're like fathers to the little ones, setting
an example and sharing out the light. Anything
with suckers or wounds needed removing, growing
twisted was punishable by chainsaw. Only straight
trees with harmonious branches and beautiful deep
crowns were selected as trees of the future. Trunk
foragers and their prey prefer them, woodpeckers
would rather ricketick their homes in them, a
forest without giants was as good as dead. But not
a single forest builder had ever lived to have the
enjoyment of the assistance he gave nature. What it
took, and this was no exaggeration, was the spirit of
a cathedral builder: starting something whose completion you would never see. A small adjustment,

even a footstep in the rotting leaves, picking a chanterelle, it changed the course of the next two hundred years. It could have consoled Madame Verona: looking at the trees her husband had spared and seeing how they had quietly started their climb to the sun. And maybe it consoled him too, in the seconds before he jumped, that in a century or two animals would mate and nest in a tree he had put a guard on as a sapling. Foresters are said to generally die peacefully – after all, they made life bigger than themselves.

*

'This is a deciduous tree,' said the man, a *luthier*, because that is the name cello makers much prefer being called. 'You have to realise that cellos are made from conifers. Preferably spruce.' Madame Verona knew very well what cellos were made from, no one needed to lecture her on that score. Norway spruce for the body, felled in the Carpathians at the end of winter, when the flow of sap had come almost to a standstill. Maple for the scroll, ebony for the pegs, Brazil wood for the bow. But her mind was made up, she wanted a cello from the wood of the tree her husband had hanged himself from.

'All right, but if your instrument ends up sounding like a cheese grater, it's on your head.'

And there was *one* other obstacle. Green wood has a mind of its own, sculptors know all about that. They scour shipyards in search of scrapped boats with weary masts. Because wood gives up its fight slowly, even if it's just to carve a beautiful face out of: it would cleave, splinter and crack if it hadn't seasoned a few years first. If a cello was going to be made from this tree, Madame Verona would be wise to summon up the patience to let the wood rest in a dry place for twenty years first.

'In that case I shall live for another twenty years, if I must.'

The cello maker, pardon, the luthier, nodded. The greatest virtuosos had commissioned him; for centuries to come people would be able to listen to

the sound of his instruments on all kinds of record-
ings, winners of international competitions refused
to play cellos that had not been made in his workshop, and he set his prices accordingly. He had
satisfied the most exacting requests, but a cello from
a deciduous tree on which a loved one had hanged
himself, that was something new. Twenty years. And
he rubbed his face, as if to feel how the years had
already marked his skin. 'It will end up being my son
who makes this cello for you, but by then he'll have
mastered the craft better than I ever did, I guarantee
you that.'

Two people among the trees, talking about what
for the trees was the trifling chasm of oh God oh
Lord twenty years.

*

It had been established long in advance that it would
be Charlo who would cut down this tree. Simply
because you'd have to go a long way to find a better
lumberjack. Once, as national champion, he'd won

the right to participate in the world wood-chopping championship, and many saw him as *the* man to break the long hegemony of the Canadians and Lapps. Nobody felled a tree with his precision. There where you wanted it, neither an inch to the left nor an inch to the right, that was where his tree would fall. But that year the world title was being fought out in the lion's den, Winnipeg, where the snot hung in stalactites from lumberjacks' noses in the winter, and if there were two things Charlo would never conquer as long as he lived, it was his fear of flying and his mistrust of foreign cooking. His dimensions were those of a healthy birch, a far too overgrown faun whose thighs stretched the largest trousers, with knees creaking from the burden and resoled shoes that never lasted more than a season. The gentlest soul in Oucwègne who, to maintain his equilibrium, cursed a random person for half an hour every day, with the dual purpose of keeping his heart and spirits light while simultaneously exercising his vocabulary. The latter was something that foresters couldn't take for granted – their silences were too long and too frequent, unused as they were to human company. When pretty girls went by they didn't whistle, they rustled. Now he stared at the tree, knowing that Monsieur Potter had hanged himself from it, and asked Madame Verona if she was sure.

He picked up his chainsaw, choked.

*

Silence is often more intense after its return. When a tree accepts its defeat, creaks and capsizes, all life flies up and off. There's crowing and cawing, branches crack, it rains feathers and down, rabbits flee to their underground shelters. All things considered, the titan's contact with the actual ground is quiet; people generally expect it to be louder. It's mainly the rest of the forest that kicks up a fuss and makes a racket. And once the creatures have assessed the damage, silence comes back. Eyes and leaves turn to the light that has never shone so brightly here. A place has come free, the struggle can begin, because the space will be occupied, by something or someone. It's like that for trees, it's like that for people.

Slow as a hearse, a truck that a tree trunk has been winched up onto drives through the streets, and people should overtake it with the same respect: calmly, without beeping. A veil of grief fell over Oucwègne that afternoon when its inhabitants saw that particular tree being carted off, as if Monsieur Potter was being buried for a second time. No signs of the cross were made and no heads were bared, but people's thoughts were gloomy and for a moment their stomachs felt empty. But a place had come free: with that tree Madame Verona was clearing away a big part of her past, to the well-concealed delight of every celibate. But that tree was going to return as a cello, they heard that soon enough from Charlo. There was no lover to smooth the path for them; it had not been a memento that needed clearing. Whereupon someone mumbled, roughly, 'If she doesn't watch out, she'll grow shut between the legs.' And it didn't occur to any of them that there might have been nothing else that could have made Madame Verona happier than being allowed to grow shut between the legs, to hold tight to what had once gone in that way.

XV

Pedants would chide her and tell her that she had made a home for herself in her own bad poem, where love is beyond time and space and even bigger, where existence has been uncoupled from all the laws that Newton and Co. ever racked their brains over, suggesting the unbearable conclusion that love was not part of existence. And yet… Still. For all that her lover had died, departed was a word she couldn't bring to bear. Although her ideas were far removed from the ones psychics had used many times to fleece the inconsolable – she *wanted* to be inconsolable –

they too came down to Monsieur Potter accompany-
ing her wherever she went.

When she looked out the window at the valley,
she looked with him. When she ate, she ate with him.
That was partly why she never urged visitors to stay
for dinner, preferring the intimacy of the idea and
feeling of dining alone with her husband. Just the
two of them, and a bottle that proceeded towards its
original emptiness half as fast as before. She was
aware that she sometimes spoke to him out loud
in the process; it wasn't as if words slipped out to
confront her with the pain of her loss. There was no
madness at work here, there were never any complete
conversations. It was short sentences. Now and then.
'Oh honey, a warm bath would do me the world of
good.' Or, 'My student, Bossart, you remember, he
played piano today as if he was typing out another
essay.' Once again: she didn't expect him to jump up
to run a bath for her, or entertain her by immediately
giving an impression of a typist at a piano keyboard.
She loved speaking in the tone she used to use when

talking to him, a specific tone she had developed during their time together, a tone she had never adopted with anyone else and had come to miss in her voice. Missing him, she had begun to miss qualities of her own; revisiting them made him seem within reach.

She sought what others find in an embrace by putting on his clothes. Especially the baggy polo-neck jumpers he had taken to wearing after he started being embarrassed by the scar the removal of a bad mole had left on his neck. Of course she felt like she was making his death absolute the first time she put his jumpers in the washing machine, something she postponed for as long as possible, only to discover to her delight that his smell had survived the assault of the washing powder.

Of all the things that were still possible, this was her favourite: in the armchair, her nose buried under his turned-up collar, reading a book. After five pages she invariably wondered what she had just read but never considered flicking back to pick up the story.

It wasn't so much the reading she loved as the act of reading, sitting there in his clothes, as if sitting in him, and knowing that another day had become part of the past and she was enjoying, *with him*, the little time that people can spend in supreme uselessness.

The men of Oucwègne who came up to do odd jobs said the same thing, Monsieur Potter is still there in that house! Thriller writers who cater for the human need for fear would seize upon this fact as an opportunity to discuss ghosts and spectral illusions. Deploying all the stylistic devices they had at their disposal in an attempt to explain something whose only explanation lies in its inexplicableness. They were only too glad to come, the men of Oucwègne, and seized upon the leaking roof or broken lamp or whatever it might be as an alibi to test their charms, bringing up the subject of what a waste it was to be lonely. They always set out with firm resolve, but once they'd made it into the house their hearts were in their boots because – despite knowing little of love

– they knew enough to see that *here* Madame Verona was still living off the interest.

*

It was the nights, leaden and too long, that stood in the way of her illusions. The house stood ricketier and ricketier on its foundations and she knew that it would be a close call as to who needed renovating first, her or it. In bed she listened to things giving in to the wind: a roof tile, a flowerpot letting itself be pushed around the garden. But even when the wind didn't blow, the house creaked as if it was doing it of its own accord the way some people crack their knuckles to loosen their joints. If she had a stray dog in the house, at moments like these she hoped with all her heart that it felt at home and brave enough to bark or growl at anything it couldn't quite place in the echo chamber of its new surroundings. In the periods when she wasn't sheltering any dogs, she realized that she was counting on Monsieur Potter, who would get out of bed and go downstairs with heart pounding to make sure it wasn't burglars, something he had actually always known before-hand. She wasn't brave enough to go downstairs herself. And what if she did, and found herself eye to eye with a person of bad will, how would that lead to a better outcome? In moments like these her ideas about Monsieur Potter's presence were inadequate. He was dead. Dead dead. And he was dead when the thunderstorms aimed their stroboscopic lights at Oucwègne. Her powerlessness in the face of nature's rage was not diminished by his absence, no arms were able to lull her fear, not even his, but when he was still alive they had made a habit of going down the hill to get drunk whenever thunderstorms racked the night. They counted the devastating seconds between lightning and thunder as if that would make blind Fate turn away. Without him she couldn't find the courage to go down the hill and even her dogs proved useless. They crawled off into the smallest corners of the house, burying their heads under their paws in accordance with a philosophy that should in all fairness be attributed to more than just ostriches.

These storms reminded her that she was a girl from the north. People who had grown up in these hills were used to the clatter that came a couple of times a year to give nightmares to those who had been through the war. The big ones were announced by silence, the birds dropped the fioriture from their scores and joined the primordial hush. You saw the devastation approaching in the distance, the heavens spewing colours no child in the world would have grabbed out of the crayon box. The rumbling moved closer. Until finally the whole flotilla of clouds was hanging overhead for hours on end, making the village the plaything of a demented god. The heavens roared about all the things they had ever been or would ever be subjected to. No matter how many of her husband's jumpers she put on, it didn't help. During the most intense storms, she had sometimes, momentarily, considered seeking out the company of someone else, knocking on their door to say, 'Talk to me, drink with me, until the fury has passed.' But she was afraid of the false expectations she would arouse, and of the joviality of men who said, 'Just think of the flashes as a photo session. Smile!' Hard men who were allowed to be scared of nature, as long as they didn't admit it publicly.

*

In an increasingly isolated village she inhabited the most isolated house. And as far as anyone knew, it had always been inhabited by outsiders, people from elsewhere, who came here with a romantic view of isolation and paid for it later with large chunks of their mind. The villagers remembered a dreamer, almost a gypsy, who fired shots into the walls and ceilings while dancing around the rooms once madness had him in its nets. They recalled a woman who drank herself a miscarriage, hurled her empty bottles at the trees and was finally carted off in an ambulance to a place where she could go simple in pyjamas until the Lord stiffened her foolish grin and accepted her into His blissful flock. They started to repeat themselves, but no smile was safe for long in that house. Madame Verona would do well to abandon her hill, to move away. It wasn't loneliness that would soften her brains, she didn't suffer from that at all. It was the solitariness, which she refused to give up. She was alone and alone to stay. Because only alone can a person remember the person attuned to two.

XVI

Of all the reasons girls young and old have for lovingly and beautifully spreading their legs, playing the cello has received by far the least attention and here too precious little of that shortfall will be made up.

*

A life should last love's length and no longer, and a shiver passed through Madame Verona's body when they informed her that the second layer of varnish had been applied to her instrument, which was more or less to say that twenty years had passed since the felling of the tree. They had been the slowest years of her existence, cribbed from exhaustion and forced upon her by the dogs that kept getting lost until they found a new mistress to guard. But the years had passed, adding themselves to the mulch of the past, where they would still have a little time to compost into memory.

She had grown old, but not effortlessly, the way a book on a shelf grows old. She was old, definitely; she had had enough of everything, long since, and she realized she could grow even older. Another twenty years could easily be added to her life, thirty even, forty if Fortuna's caprice showed her no mercy. Mother Nature is like that; she picks out a few random creatures here and there to motivate the young to live even more recklessly out of disgust for decrepitude, and Madame Verona was increasingly suited to that macabre role.

She could still get up and down the hill, and would be able to manage it for a while yet. But she had started taking longer over the climb and paused more often on the way, resting her bags on the ground and gasping for breath. Each subsequent climb would be slower than the one before; the account had been opened, the tendency had become a certainty. Those who still regularly conversed had others to point out the start of their decline, flagged by the way they repeated themselves more quickly, forgetting what they had just said. Madame Verona only had herself to catch her out when, more and more often, she left the same sentences unsaid.

It wasn't the mirror that insulted her or the hair she found on her pillowcase in the morning, but her dreams, which, although renowned for being able to twist reality into a plausible unreality, were unable to succeed in making Monsieur Potter grow old with her. If she dreamed about him, and that wasn't something she looked forward to, it was as the man she had known. A young man. And the woman he took in his young arms in her dreams was her: an old woman. She found it repugnant. But the subconscious takes no offence at bad taste and never woke her before the dream had been dreamed to completion. She hated the illogicality of it. Love was the one and the many; she had thought that her lover growing old in time with her would have at least been dreamable.

Yes, it had come as a shock when the cello maker informed her that the instrument would be delivered to her home the next day. It wasn't so much the thinning out of the calendar that made her shudder as the fact that she had proved so capable of surviving without him these twenty years. It was the dogs that always came to offer themselves, almost as if they were doing it to give *her* the pleasure of caring for someone or something rather than to satisfy any needs of their own. If she was being honest, Madame Verona would admit that she had used that constant supply of dogs to stay alive, as if they were her only valid excuse. It was a betrayal – one no one would hold against her – of an alliance, of sacraments holier than marriage.

*

That cello: it was ugly, as expected. The hand of the craftsman was unmistakable, a master who had produced a minor miracle with the inferior materials foisted upon him. But compared with cellos made of the right kinds of wood, this was a monstrosity and she felt guilty towards the maker, who had worked on it for years in the full knowledge that this instrument was an insult to his talent. Of course, she had been warned and the warning had proved superfluous. She had known what to expect, but expectations arose to be disappointed, and that was why it hurt her so much to realize that for once they had been fulfilled so exactly. From scroll to tailpiece a failure, and as much a cello as a banjo can be a guitar.

She put the instrument in a corner of the room, unplayed, because if there was one thing she had few illusions about it was the sound. She was all too familiar with the vanity of luthiers, often justified, who were fond of playing a few bars for their customers. A little Boccherini, a touch of Bach. To demonstrate the sound, but at the same time wanting to prove that they were more than just cabinet-makers. As if to say, 'Hey, we quarter sawed the boards and let them dry. We went to check them every day, for years, mind you, and spoke to them as unabashedly as a gardener greeting his roses. We assembled this instrument with the utmost preci-sion. And all because we know the beauty it serves. Listen.' With a careless hand they would brush aside all compliments about the excellence of their playing. 'Come now, you're exaggerating,' they would say, 'I'm just a simple carpenter,' preferring that word now even to luthier, seeing as it has often been carpenters who, in the fringes of the history of literature, have enjoyed the privilege of standing at the cradle of a miracle: Joseph, Geppetto. And meanwhile they puff up their chests with pride, ready to return home with a levity that will make their wives cheerful. But not once had this cello maker bowed the strings by way of demonstration; he hadn't even casually plucked a single string. One wondered whether he had even dared to test his merchandise in the workshop, anxious perhaps to retain the benefit of the doubt.

Look in any reference book on the theory of music and it will tell you that, more than any other instrument, the cello is closest to the human voice. It doesn't take an especially developed ear to realize that this statement flatters the human voice. No shortage of ugly voices, but if there was one cello anywhere that could approach human croaking and droning, this would be it. The only thing was, who wanted to hear it?

*

The cello had stood there for weeks in a corner of the room, dead furniture, when Madame Verona suddenly opened the windows and took it between her legs.

The smell of rosin and all it evoked…

*

She bowed the strings for the first time, as if cutting someone's throat with a knife. People with a less misanthropic imagination might prefer to limit the simile to a mother cutting slices of bread – why not, that image too can be part of the reality. As long as it's cutting. She cut a second time, not even hoping she was mistaken, but to hear again what had never been in doubt: the ugly sound, the disappointing resonance, the miserable timbre. Perhaps she was looking for something beautiful in that ugliness – after all, ugly things often present that possibility – trying to find some way of turning the instrument's failings to her hand. Someone with a sarcastic disposition would have known what to do with this cello, that was obvious. Our characterization of Madame Verona in these pages has been careless if the immediate conclusion is that sarcasm was a thing she did not appreciate. She had no aversion to the sentiment and had, in the past, used it unsparingly. That was why she realized that sarcasm was a form of laziness, a house that was open to the unenlightened, and an emotion that would have been completely out of place in this situation.

She played. It sounded ugly, but she played. Fauré. The pieces she had played with her lover at the academy, but now her cheeks weren't red. She pressed herself tight against the instrument to feel the vibrations. And if she closed her eyes, it was not to enjoy the results of her own fingering, but to hear the piano that Monsieur Potter would have played to accompany her. That was how she would do it every evening from now on. She would sit at the window with legs spread and play the cello. An ensemble that wasn't, a duet with absence. Talking to the non-existent, which might be the only correct definition of very deep prayer.

XVII

There are but few occasions on which it is permissible to use the phrase 'fatal day' and a littérateur worth his salt would seize them with both hands. In this case, however, he would be exaggerating and drawing attention to his own bluff. It was true that fatal days could begin with radio reports of imminent and heavy snow; ask any film director. They could easily begin the way this February day began: with a few council workers taking the precaution of closing the difficult hill road, dragging on their fags, then treating themselves to a break in the back of the van, sharing the provisions their wives had wrapped in cling film and poured into thermoses for them that morning.

Madame Verona had got up without plans and was greeted by her tail-wagging dog. She had eaten breakfast with the radio on and heard what she herself could have predicted with considerably less effort, that there would be a momentous snowfall that would make the roads virtually impassable. It was often like that in late February: encouraged by the slowly lengthening days, birds cautiously sung their territories, trees budded and creatures that had buried themselves for the winter got ready to be reunited with the sun. And that was the very moment the winter slammed in one last time, to purge the world of idiots. Toads, horny as hell, that began their nocturnal marches when it was moist and around eight degrees, were able to meet their maker without even needing a car to squash them. The last, bitter winter offensive was a death sentence for premature joie de vivre, existence was reserved for those who always arrived everywhere a little too late. Only mankind shepherded its idiots through winter's last attack, offering up a handful of flu-bitten pensioners in exchange.

After listening to the weather report, Madame Verona washed herself, but not like someone who is expected somewhere. And then she lit the fire as carefully as an enthusiastic Brownie jockeying for Brown Owl's approval. Of course she had watched her woodpile shrink to an alarming minimum and her mind had raced as she carried the last ten pieces of wood inside in a basket. But it wasn't until she was pushing the last log into the fire that she drew her conclusion, calmly, in complete tranquillity. She put on her coat, which confused the dog but also cheered him up, glad as he was to interrupt his daily routine with a walk.

She had always taken her dogs out hiking with her, all except this one. This one had come into her life after abandoning his farmyard in a lather of lust, searching for a partner for a quick mate and losing his good sense and the way back in the process. And seizing the opportunity to find a better master. Judging by his appetite he had been on the road for days, and the sleep that he finally gave in to after his meal lasted for days as well, interrupted only occasionally by his turning over with a sigh. When he awoke from it, he immediately placed himself at the service of his hostess, making this clear by barking at postmen and pigeons that dared to alight on the terrace. No one missed him; the animal shelter hadn't had anyone drop by looking for their great lump of a dog, and the posters that occasionally adorned the streets, hung up mainly by dejected children, only ever showed snaps of permed, almost woollen little doggies.

Madame Verona was willing to let him stay, as long as he realized his future grave would not be located in a corner of the garden of this house. It was a temporary solution, considering his youth. He didn't need to entertain any illusions about going for walks with Madame Verona as well. He had a garden and it was big enough for him to stretch his legs and relieve himself in. The animal had long since resigned himself to the course of events, which explains his surprise when Madame Verona, after adding the last piece of wood to the fire, put on her coat and beckoned him to the door. The prospect of finally being able to empty his shrunken bladder on posts, letterboxes and car wheels elicited his most charming bark and would have had him ramming his mistress's legs with joy except that he realized she was too old for that kind of doggery, and that it would most likely lead to his having the implantation of a plastic hip on his conscience.

*

They walked. It was slow, but they walked. From the door to the forest path. The steep forest path. Many people would have looked back one last time, casting a last glance at the house. The site of love and mourning. Not Madame Verona. She took another step downhill. Ten paces later she turned to call the dog, which had stayed standing on the hilltop as if he, the shepherd, had realized very well that she would never make it back up. But she called him and he followed her, after a bark that could have been his last.

We know that, after reaching the valley, they sat down on a bench. We know that it started to snow. And we know that Madame Verona finally permitted herself a short walk to warm up a little, and that the dog followed her again. Her journey ended under the plane tree on the village square, the location of the pétanque field which had given rise to decades of discussions about vitally important millimetres. Where the river took up the singing men's froth and the smell of frying fish attracted stray cats. She sat down on one of the rocks and could imagine how much she would have enjoyed a cigarette at that moment, although she had never smoked. Pity, a packet of her husband's was still up at the house.

The dog lay down on her feet, either from

helpfulness, hoping to transform himself into an extra pair of socks for his increasingly hypothermic mistress, or from fear. It didn't help having Madame Verona say to him every now and then, 'Go away, boy! Go find a home!' He stayed lying there, more faithful in the face of death than she herself had ever had the courage to be. And who was she to give him a kick to get rid of him? Maybe a car would stop after all to present them with a lift. In that case Madame Verona would stay sitting, no question of that, but offer the people the dog. That possibility was the only thing she had left to anticipate. Beyond it lay the Nothing we can all imagine ourselves one day entering with a sense of déjà vu. The last moments of a life, and she found it no strain at all to think once again about her lover. Just a little bit longer and that Nothing would embrace her, but with arms that could also be his. That was how a smile came to be found in the morning, frozen on a face that was turned to the realm of fables. The face of someone who is greeting a doorman and proceeding to a front desk where she will answer the most important question by saying that she has been lucky enough to attract dogs, her whole life long.